CARNEGIE LEARNING MATH SERIES
LEVEL 3

STUDENT EDITION
VOLUME 1

Carnegie Learning >

300815

GEORGE J. RYAN JUNIOR HIGH SCHOOL - 216 Q
94-20 175th STREET
FLUSHING, NEW YORK 11365

Carnegie Learning >

437 Grant St., Suite 2000
Pittsburgh, PA 15219
Phone 412.690.2442
Customer Service Phone 877.401.2527
Fax 412.690.2444

www.carnegielearning.com

Chapter 1 © istockphoto.com/Tony Campbell;
Chapter 2 © istockphoto.com/Brendan Hunter;
Chapter 3 © istockphoto.com/Gorfer;
Chapter 4 © istockphoto.com/Kevin Lohka;
Chapter 5 © istockphoto.com/TheCrimsonMonkey;
Chapter 6 © istockphoto.com/loops7;
Chapter 7 © istockphoto.com/emmgunn;
Chapter 8 © istockphoto.com/Roberto A Sanchez;
Chapter 9 © istockphoto.com/stevedangers;
Chapter 10 © istockphoto.com/Hans Laubel;
Chapter 11 © istockphoto.com/Claude Dagenais;
Chapter 12 © istockphoto.com/mountainberryphoto;
Chapter 13 © istockphoto.com/David Wood;
Chapter 14 © istockphoto.com/yurok;
Chapter 15 © istockphoto.com/Vallentin Vassileff;
Chapter 16 © istockphoto.com/Rosemarie Gearhart;
Chapter 17 © istockphoto.com/Christopher Futcher

Copyright © 2011 by Carnegie Learning, Inc. All rights reserved. *Carnegie Learning, Cognitive Tutor, SchoolCare,* and *Learning by Doing* are all registered marks of Carnegie Learning, Inc. All other company and product names mentioned are used for identification purposes only and may be trademarks of their respective owners. Permission is granted for photocopying rights within licensed sites only. Any other usage or reproduction in any form is prohibited without the expressed consent of the publisher.

ISBN: 978-1-60972-112-1
Student Edition, Volume 1

Printed in the United States of America
1-04/2011 HPS
2-7/2011 HPS

Dear Student,

You are about to begin an exciting journey! These mathematical materials were written specifically for *you*, a middle school student. The book you are holding is *your* book. There is lots of space for writing, sketching, drawing, cutting, pasting, and constructing new mathematical ideas. You may want to highlight key terms, take notes in the margins, or even doodle on the cover.

Connections are important in life. The popularity of social networks shows the importance of connections. In much the same way, mathematics connects with so many activities in our lives. Throughout the lessons, you will build new knowledge based upon your prior knowledge. You will apply math to real-world situations so that you can see why it's meaningful. You will encounter models that portray mathematical concepts. Models will be presented in all sorts of ways—from lesson openers, to pictures, to different student methods and approaches to problem solving. You will also use manipulatives, which are objects that you can use to model or reinforce key mathematical concepts.

Of course, if you need additional practice, you can find it in your Assignments and Skills Practice book. Keep in mind, no professional athlete practices by just playing an entire game—ballet dancers repeat some basic steps, moves, and dances; basketball players practice dribbling, shooting, and defending; even writers jot ideas for novels in their spare time—all to improve their skills. Mathematics is no different and these materials enable and encourage you to practice.

Don't worry—you will not be working alone. We encourage students to work together in pairs or in groups because it gets you talking about your insights. Everyone will share his or her ideas and thoughts in class. Sometimes you will help your classmates, and other times they will help you.

Today's workplace demands teamwork and self-confidence. At Carnegie Learning, we have designed a Math Series to help you to make the most of your math course. Enjoy the journey and share your thoughts with others. Have fun while Learning by Doing!

The Carnegie Learning® Curriculum Development Team

ACKNOWLEDGMENTS

A Note from the Authors...

You are about to begin a journey as a "powerful problem solver." Mathematics is the key to many future opportunities, and this book will teach you a range of mathematical ideas—from number to algebra, and from geometry to statistics—that are useful in many professions and careers. Math is more than memorizing "how to do something," it is solving problems in unique ways and explaining your solutions to others in verbal and written ways—just like successful career professionals! Have fun and learn a lot!

Core Authors

- William S. Hadley, Algebra and Proportional Reasoning
- Mary Lou Metz, Data Analysis and Probability
- Mary Lynn Raith, Number and Operations
- Janet Sinopoli, Algebra
- Jaclyn Snyder, Geometry and Measurement

Contributing Authors

- Janet Falkowski
- Marianne O'Connor
- Agnes Pavolovich
- Ken Labuskes
- Jennifer Panasko

Carnegie Learning Curriculum Development Team

- Sandy Bartle
  Senior Academic Officer
- Joshua Fisher
  Math Editor
- David "Augie" Rivera
  Math Editor
- David Dengler
  Director, Curriculum Development
- Jen Gansberger
  Editorial Assistant
- Lezlee Ross
  Curriculum Developer

Advisory Board

- Shelly Allen, Richmond County Schools
- Ryan Baker, Worcester Polytechnic Institute
- Bill Bush, University of Louisville
- John McCook, McCook and Associates
- Roxana Moreno, University of New Mexico
- Doug Rohrer, University of South Florida
- Bob Siegler, Carnegie Mellon University
- Mary Ann Stine, Private Consultant

Vendors

- Bookmasters, Inc.
- Mathematical Expressions
- Hess Print Solutions
- ESI Design
- Nesbitt Graphics, Inc.

Special Thanks

- Peter Arkle for the design and rendering of "The Crew."
- Richmond County School District, Georgia, for piloting lessons and providing implementation feedback.
- Carnegie Learning Managers of School Partnership for content and design review.
- The Children of Carnegie Learning employees for providing a "middle-schooler's" perspective, with special recognition to:
  - Matthew B.
  - Dawson D.
  - Allison M.
  - Adam, Nic, and Shane R.
  - Aaron and Melinda R.

Acknowledgments

TABLE OF CONTENTS

LINEAR FUNCTIONS _____41

Table of Contents

Table of Contents

Table of Contents

SIMILARITY _____ 477

Table of Contents

THE CREW

The Crew is here to help you on your journey. Sometimes they will remind you about things you already learned. Sometimes they will ask you questions to help you think about different strategies. Sometimes they will share fun facts. They are members of your group—someone you can rely on!

Teacher aides will guide you along your journey. They will help you make connections and remind you to think about the details.

MATHEMATICAL REPRESENTATIONS

Introduction

During this course, you will solve problems and work with many different representations of mathematical concepts, ideas, and processes to better understand the world. Each lesson will provide you with opportunities to discuss your ideas, work within groups, and share your solutions and methods with your class. These process icons are placed throughout the text.

Discuss to Understand

- Read the problem carefully.
- What is the context of the problem? Do we understand it?
- What is the question that we are being asked? Does it make sense?
- Is this problem similar to some other problem we know?

Think for Yourself

- Do I need any additional information to answer the question?
- Is this problem similar to some other problem that I know?
- How can I represent the problem using a picture, a diagram, symbols, or some other representation?

Work with Your Partner

- How did you do the problem?
- Show me your representation.
- This is the way I thought about the problem—how did you think about it?
- What else do we need to solve the problem?
- Does our reasoning and our answer make sense to each other?
- How will we explain our solution to the class?

Share with the Class

- Here is our solution and the methods we used.
- Are we communicating our strategies clearly?
- We could only get this far with our solution. How can we finish?
- Could we have used a different strategy to solve the problem?

Key Terms of the Course

There are important terms you will encounter throughout this book. It is important that you have an understanding of these words as you get started on your journey through the mathematical concepts. Knowing what is meant by these terms and using these terms will help you think, reason, and communicate your ideas. The Graphic Organizers shown display a definition for a key term, related words, sample questions, and examples.

DEFINITION

To study or look closely for patterns. Analyzing can involve examining or breaking a concept down into smaller parts to gain a better understanding of it.

RELATED WORDS

- examine
- evaluate
- determine
- observe
- consider
- investigate
- what do you notice?
- what do you think?
- sort and match

ASK YOURSELF

- Do I see any patterns?
- Have I seen something like this before?
- What happens if the shape, representation, or numbers change?

ANALYZE

EXAMPLE

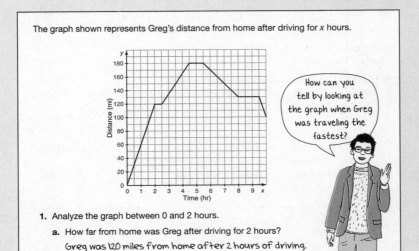

The graph shown represents Greg's distance from home after driving for *x* hours.

How can you tell by looking at the graph when Greg was traveling the fastest?

1. Analyze the graph between 0 and 2 hours.

   a. How far from home was Greg after driving for 2 hours?

   Greg was 120 miles from home after 2 hours of driving.

DEFINITION

To give details or describe how to determine an answer or solution.
Explaining your reasoning helps justify conclusions.

RELATED WORDS

- show your work
- explain your calculation
- justify
- why or why not?

ASK YOURSELF

- How should I organize my thoughts?
- Is my explanation logical?
- Does my reasoning make sense?
- How can I justify my answer to others?

Don't forget to check your answers!

EXPLAIN YOUR REASONING

EXAMPLE

Read each context and decide whether it fits the definition of a function.
Explain your reasoning.

1. *Input:* The basketball team has numbered uniforms.
   Output: Each player wears a uniform with her assigned number.

   Yes. Each player wears one uniform with one specific number.

2. *Input:* Janelle sends a text message to everyone in her contact list on her cell phone.
   Output: There are 41 friends and family on Janelle's contact list.

   No. One text message is mapped to 41 people.

DEFINITION

To display information in various ways. Representing mathematics can be done using words, tables, graphs, or symbols.

RELATED WORDS

- show
- sketch
- draw
- create
- plot
- graph
- write an equation
- complete the table

ASK YOURSELF

- How should I organize my thoughts?
- How do I use this model to show a concept or idea?
- What does this representation tell me?
- Is my representation accurate?

REPRESENT

EXAMPLE

The linear graph shown is a model of a skier's elevation, over time, while skiing down a hill.

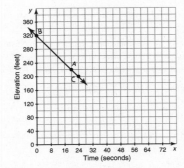

1. What does point A on the graph represent?

Point A represents that after 20 seconds, the skier is at an elevation of 220 feet.

DEFINITION

To make an educated guess based on the analysis of given data.
Estimating first helps inform reasoning.

RELATED WORDS

- predict
- approximate
- expect
- about how much?

ASK YOURSELF

- Does my reasoning make sense?
- Is my solution close to my estimation?

Estimating gets you in the neighborhood, calculating gets you the address.

ESTIMATE

EXAMPLE

Remember, you can use **estimation** to determine the approximate values before you do actual calculations to get a sense of the answer.

For example, you can estimate the difference of 125.35 and 84.95. So, you could round 125.35 down to 125, and round 84.95 up to 85. Then, calculate the difference of 125 and 85, to $125 - 85 = 40$.

You can write this as $125.35 - 84.95 \approx 40$.

The symbol $\approx$ means "is approximately equal to."

4. Estimate the value of each expression.
   a. $748.75 + 60.22$

   $750 + 60 = 810$
   $748.75 + 60.22 \approx 810$

DEFINITION

To represent or give an account of in words. Describing communicates mathematical ideas to others.

RELATED WORDS

- demonstrate
- label
- display
- compare
- define
- determine
- what are the advantages?
- what are the disadvantages?
- what is similar?
- what is different?

ASK YOURSELF

- How should I organize my thoughts?
- Is my explanation logical?
- Did I consider the context of the situation?
- Does my reasoning make sense?

DESCRIBE

EXAMPLE

This past summer you were hired to work at a custom T-shirt shop, U.S. Shirts. One of your responsibilities is to calculate the total cost of customers' orders. The shop charges $8 per shirt plus a one-time charge of $15 to set up a T-shirt design.

1. Describe the problem situation and your responsibility in your own words.

   I will calculate the total cost of orders. The total cost of an order is the cost of each shirt ordered plus a setup fee. The cost of one shirt is $8, and the setup fee is $15.

Problem Types You Will See

Worked Example

When you see a Worked Example:
- ▶ Take your time to read through it,
- ▶ Question your own understanding, and
- ▶ Think about the connections between steps.

Ask yourself:
- ▶ What is the main idea?
- ▶ How would this work if I changed the numbers?
- ▶ Have I used these strategies before?

Two different examples of ways to solve the same two-step equation are shown.

	Method 1	Method 2
	$2m - 6 = 22$	$2m - 6 = 22$
Step 1:	$2m - 6 + 6 = 22 + 6$	$\underline{+ 6 = + 6}$
	$2m = 28$	$2m = 28$
Step 2:	$\dfrac{2m}{2} = \dfrac{28}{2}$	$\dfrac{2m}{2} = \dfrac{28}{2}$
	$m = 14$	$m = 14$

1. Describe the inverse operations used in each step.

   Step 1: A 6 was added to both sides of the equation to undo the subtraction.

   Step 2: A 2 was divided by both sides to undo the multiplication.

2. What is the difference between the strategies used to solve the equation?

   In method 1, the first inverse operation is written horizontally. In method 2, the first inverse operation is written vertically.

3. Verify the solution is $m = 14$.

   $2(14) - 6 = 22$
   $28 - 6 = 22$
   $22 = 22$

Thumbs Down

When you see a Thumbs Down icon:

▶ Take your time to read through the *incorrect* solution.

▶ Think about what error was made.

Ask yourself:

▶ Where is the error?

▶ Why is it an error?

▶ How can I correct it?

Ron has a player's card for the arcade at the mall. His player's card keeps track of the number of credits he earns as he wins games. Each winning game earns the same number of credits, and those credits can be redeemed for various prizes. Ron has been saving his credits to collect a prize worth 500 credits.

The table shows the number of credits Ron had on his game card at various times today when he checked his balance at the arcade.

Number of Games Ron Won Today	Number of Credits on Ron's Player's Card
0	120
12	216
18	264
25	320
40	440

1. Analyze Rhonda's calculations shown.

$$\frac{440 \text{ credits}}{40 \text{ games won}} = \frac{11 \text{ credits}}{1 \text{ game won}}$$

I used the last listing in the table and wrote a rate: $\frac{\text{credits}}{\text{games won}}$.

Then, I divided both the first and second terms by 40 to write the rate as a unit rate. I got $\frac{11}{1}$. The unit rate is 11 credits per each game won.

Explain to Rhonda why her calculations are incorrect.

Rhonda did not take into account that Ron already had 120 credits saved on his card before he started winning today. The 40 games he won today earned him only 320 credits (440 – 120).

Thumbs Up

When you see a Thumbs Up icon:

▶ Take your time to read through the *correct* solution.

▶ Think about the connections between steps.

Ask yourself:

▶ Why is this method correct?

▶ Have I used this method before?

Problem Types

Carlos and Tonya are given the problem $1.2 \times 10^3 + 5.3 \times 10^5$. Each solves it correctly, but in different ways.

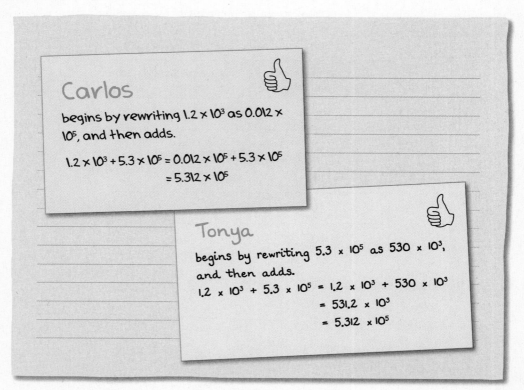

Carlos

begins by rewriting 1.2×10^3 as 0.012×10^5, and then adds.

$$1.2 \times 10^3 + 5.3 \times 10^5 = 0.012 \times 10^5 + 5.3 \times 10^5$$
$$= 5.312 \times 10^5$$

Tonya

begins by rewriting 5.3×10^5 as 530×10^3, and then adds.

$$1.2 \times 10^3 + 5.3 \times 10^5 = 1.2 \times 10^3 + 530 \times 10^3$$
$$= 531.2 \times 10^3$$
$$= 5.312 \times 10^5$$

10. How are their methods similar? How are their methods different?

Each person converted one of the two numbers in scientific notation to have the same exponent as the other number. Each chose a different number; Carlos converted the first term and Tonya converted the second term of the original addition problem.

Who's Correct?

When you see a Who's Correct? icon:

▶ Take your time to read through the situation.

▶ Question the strategy or reason given.

▶ Determine correct or not correct.

Ask yourself:

▶ Does the reasoning make sense?

▶ If the reasoning makes sense, what is the justification?

▶ If the reasoning does not make sense, what error was made?

Problem 2   Rise and Then Run

The ratio $\frac{\text{rise}}{\text{run}}$ was used either correctly or incorrectly to determine the rate of change in the following graphs shown. Each graph models the same problem.

● Follow the arrows to write the rate of change.

● Explain any errors in the process of drawing the arrows.

1.

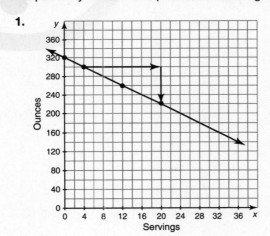

$\dfrac{16 \text{ servings}}{-80 \text{ ounces}}$

Incorrect. The run was drawn first.

1 LINEAR EQUATIONS

Black bears, like this little cub, are really good climbers. They climb trees to eat and to avoid their enemies. There are all kinds of different black bears: New Mexico black bears, Florida black bears, Louisiana black bears . . .

A PARK RANGER'S WORK IS NEVER DONE

Solving Problems Using Equations

Learning Goal

In this lesson, you will:

▶ Write and solve two-step equations to represent problem situations.

▶ Solve two-step equations.

Key Terms

▶ inverse operations

▶ two-step equation

▶ solution

▶ coefficient

▶ constant

▶ Properties of Equality

The first equations to ever be written down using symbolic notation are much like the equations you will study in this lesson. They first appeared in a book called the Whetstone of Witte by Robert Recorde in 1557. This book is notable because it contained the first recorded use of the equals sign. Recorde got tired of writing the words "is equal to" in all his equations so he decided that a pair of parallel lines of the same length sitting sideways would be the perfect symbol because, as he said, "no two things can be more equal." Here are the first two equations ever written:

$$14x + 15 = 71$$

$$20x - 18 = 102$$

Can you solve the world's oldest symbolic equations?

Problem 1   Building a Walkway

Many situations can be modeled by equations that need more than one operation to solve them.

1. At a local national park, the park rangers decide that they want to extend a wooden walkway through the forest to encourage people to stay on the path. The existing walkway is 150 feet long. The park rangers believe that they can build the additional walkway at a rate of about 5 feet per hour.

   a. How many total feet of walkway will there be after the park rangers work for 5 hours?

   b. How many total feet of walkway will there be after the park rangers work for 7 hours?

   c. Define a variable for the amount of time that the rangers will work. Then, use the variable to write an expression that represents the total number of feet of walkway built, given the amount of time that the rangers will work.

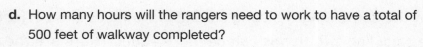

Can you imagine how long 500 feet is? It's about $1\frac{2}{3}$ football fields.

How can the expression you wrote in part (c) help you?

   d. How many hours will the rangers need to work to have a total of 500 feet of walkway completed?

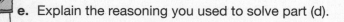

   e. Explain the reasoning you used to solve part (d).

   f. What mathematical operations did you perform to calculate your answer to part (d)?

g. Write an equation that you can use to determine the amount of time the rangers need to build a total of 500 feet of walkway. Then, determine the value of the variable that will make this equation true.

h. Interpret your answer in terms of this problem situation.

2. How many hours will the rangers need to work to build a total of 270 feet of walkway? Explain your reasoning.

a. What mathematical operations did you perform to determine your answer?

Don't forget to take a minute to estimate your answer before starting to work.

b. Explain why using these mathematical operations gives you the correct answer.

c. Write an equation that you can use to determine the amount of time it will take to have a total of 270 feet of walkway completed.

d. Determine the value of the variable that will make this equation true.

e. Interpret your answer in terms of this problem situation.

3. How many hours will the rangers need to work to build a total of 100 feet of walkway? Explain your reasoning.

a. What mathematical operations did you perform to determine your answer?

b. Write an equation that you can use to determine the amount of time it will take to have a total of 100 feet of walkway completed.

c. Determine the value of the variable that will make this equation true.

Does your answer make sense?

d. Interpret your answers in terms of this problem situation.

Problem 2   Rescuing a Bear Cub

1. Part of a park ranger's job is to perform rescue missions for people and animals. Suppose that a bear cub has fallen into a steep ravine on the park grounds. The cub is 77 feet below the surface of the ground in the ravine. A ranger coaxed the cub to climb into a basket attached to a rope and is pulling up the cub at a rate of 7 feet per minute.

a. How many feet below the surface of the ground will the cub be in 6 minutes?

b. How many feet below the surface of the ground will the cub be in 11 minutes?

c. Define a variable for the amount of time spent pulling the cub up the ravine. Then use the variable to write an expression that represents the number of feet below the surface of the ground the cub is, given the number of minutes that the ranger has spent pulling up the cub.

d. In how many minutes will the cub be 14 feet from the surface?

e. Explain your reasoning you used to solve part (d).

f. What mathematical operations did you perform to determine your answer to part (d)?

g. Explain why using these mathematical operations gives you the correct answer.

h. Write an equation that you can use to determine the number of minutes it takes for the cub to be 14 feet below the surface of the ground by setting the expression you wrote in part (c) equal to 14. Then determine the value of the variable that will make the equation true.

2. In how many minutes will the cub be 28 feet from the surface?

a. Explain your reasoning.

b. What mathematical operations did you perform to determine your answer?

c. Explain why using these mathematical operations gives you the correct answer.

d. Write an equation that you can use to determine the number of feet below the surface of the ground that the cub will be in 28 minutes. Then, determine the value of the variable that will make the equation true.

Problem 3   Solving Two-Step Equations

In Problems 1 and 2, you were solving two-step equations. To solve two-step equations you need to perform *inverse operations*. **Inverse operations** are operations that "undo" each other. For example, adding 3 and subtracting 3 are inverse operations. **Two-step equations** are equations that require two inverse operations to solve. A **solution** to an equation is any value for a variable that makes the equation true.

Let's consider the equation:

$$2m - 6 = 22$$

The left side of this equation has two terms separated by the subtraction operation. The 2 in the first term of the left side of the equation is called the *coefficient*. A **coefficient** is the number that is multiplied by a variable. The terms 6 and 22 are called *constants*. A **constant** is a term that does not change in value.

Remember, when you are solving equations you must maintain balance.

When solving any equation, you want to get the variable by itself on one side of the equals sign.

Two different examples of ways to solve the same two-step equation are shown.

	Method 1	Method 2
	$2m - 6 = 22$	$2m - 6 = 22$
Step 1:	$2m - 6 + 6 = 22 + 6$	$\underline{+\ 6 = +\ 6}$
	$2m = 28$	$2m = 28$
Step 2:	$\dfrac{2m}{2} = \dfrac{28}{2}$	$\dfrac{2m}{2} = \dfrac{28}{2}$
	$m = 14$	$m = 14$

1. Describe the inverse operations used in each step.

    Step 1:

    Step 2:

2. What is the difference between the strategies used to solve the equation?

3. Verify the solution is $m = 14$.

> What are the general strategies to solve any two-step equation?

4. Solve each two-step equation. Show your work.

    a. $5v - 34 = 26$ **b.** $3x + 7 = 37$

c. $23 + 4x = 83$

d. $2.5c - 12 = 13$

e. $\dfrac{3}{4}x + 2 = 4\dfrac{2}{3}$

f. $-\dfrac{2}{3}b + \dfrac{2}{5} = 6\dfrac{4}{5}$

Don't forget to check your solution. Substitute your answer back into the original equation and make sure it is true.

1

g. $-\dfrac{t}{5} - 9 = 21$

h. $2 = 2.27 - \dfrac{s}{4}$

i. $12m - 17 = 139$

j. $121.1 = -19.3 - 4d$

k. $-23z + 234 = 970$ **l.** $7685 = 345 - 5d$

Talk the Talk

The **Properties of Equality** allow you to balance and solve equations involving any number.

Properties of Equality	For all numbers *a*, *b*, and *c*, ...
Addition Property of Equality	If $a = b$, then $a + c = b + c$.
Subtraction Property of Equality	If $a = b$, then $a - c = b - c$.
Multiplication Property of Equality	If $a = b$, then $ac = bc$.
Division Property of Equality	If $a = b$ and $c \neq 0$, then $\frac{a}{c} = \frac{b}{c}$.

1. Describe the strategies you can use to solve any two-step equation.

2. Describe a solution to any equation.

Be prepared to share your solutions and methods.

WHY DOESN'T THIS WORK?

Equations with Infinite or No Solutions

Learning Goals

In this lesson, you will:

▶ Identify and solve equations that have infinite solutions.

▶ Identify and solve equations that have no solutions.

Some things are always true, and some things are never true. And sometimes, using math, we can discover things that are always true or never true that are somewhat surprising.

The Meteorologists' Theorem is a good example of a surprising result that is always true. This theorem tells us that there are always two places directly opposite each other on Earth that have the exact same temperature.

What other things can you think of that are always true in math? How about never true?

Problem 1 Interpreting Solutions

Amy and Damon were solving an equation from their math homework. They came across the equation shown.

$$3x + 7 = 5x + 2(3-x) + 1$$

Amy

$$3x + 7 = 5x + 2(3 - x) + 1$$
$$3x - 5x + 7 = 5x - 5x + 2(3 - x) + 1$$
$$-2x + 7 = 2(3 - x) + 1$$
$$-2x + 7 = 6 + (-2x) + 1$$
$$-2x + 7 = 7 + (-2x)$$
$$-2x + 2x + 7 = 7 + (-2x) + 2x$$
$$7 = 7$$

> What happened to the term with the variable?

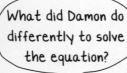

> What did Damon do differently to solve the equation?

Damon

$$3x + 7 = 5x + 2(3 - x) + 1$$
$$3x + 7 = 5x + 6 + (-2x) + 1$$
$$3x + 7 = 5x + (-2x) + 6 + 1$$
$$3x + 7 = 3x + 7$$
$$3x + 7 + (-7) = 3x + 7 + (-7)$$
$$\frac{3x}{3} = \frac{3x}{3}$$
$$x = x$$

> What happened to all the constants?

1. Explain why both Amy's and Damon's methods are correct, but have different solutions.

2. How would you interpret the final equation in each solution? Is the final equation always true, sometimes true, or never true? Explain your reasoning.

3. Complete the table by substituting the given values of x into the expressions from each side of the equation and evaluate them. Show your work.

x	$3x + 7$	$5x + 2(3 - x) + 1$
−5		
−3		
1		
4		

4. Based on the results from evaluating each row, does it appear that the expressions are equivalent? Explain your reasoning.

You can also use a graphing calculator to determine if the expressions are equivalent. Follow the steps provided to graph the expression $3x + 7$.

Step 1: Press ⬛ **Y=** . Your cursor should be blinking on the line \\Y$_1$=. Enter the equation. To enter a variable like x, Press ⬛ **X, T, θ, *n*** once.

Step 2: Press ⬛ **WINDOW** to set the bounds and intervals you want displayed.

```
WINDOW
   X min  =  -10
   X max  =   10
   X scl  =    1
   Y min  =  -10
   Y max  =   10
   Y scl  =    1
```

> The way you set the Window will vary each time depending on the equation you are graphing.

The **Xmin** represents the least point on the x-axis that will be seen on the screen. The **Xmax** represents the greatest point that will be seen on the x-axis. Lastly, the **Xscl** represents the intervals.

These same intervals are also used for the y-axis (**Ymin**, **Ymax**, and **Yscl**). Set the **Xmin** to -10. Set the **Xmax** to 10 and lastly set the interval to 1. Use the same settings for the y-axis.

Step 3: Press [**GRAPH**].

Your graphing calculator should display the screen shown.

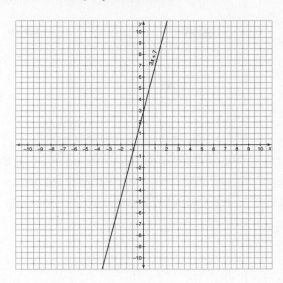

Next, graph the second expression from the table.

Press [**Y=**] and go to Y_2 and enter $5x + 2(3 - x) + 1$. Then, move your cursor to the left of Y_2 and press [**ENTER**] one time to change the way the line will be displayed. Finally, press [**GRAPH**].

5. Sketch the graph on the coordinate plane shown.

Based on the information from your table, can you predict how the graph will look?

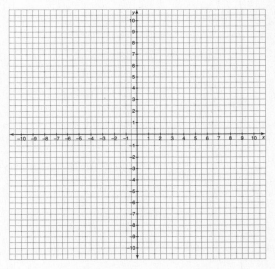

Set your bounds on your calculator like the bounds are shown on the grid.

6. What do you notice about each graph? What does this mean in terms of a value of x for which these expressions are equivalent?

7. Amy says, "Since the expressions are equivalent, then the equation is true for all values of the variable. This means that there are an infinite number of solutions to this equation." Is Amy correct? Explain your reasoning.

Problem 2 Okay, But What About This One?

Consider this new equation:

$$3(x - 5) + 11 = x + 2(x + 5)$$

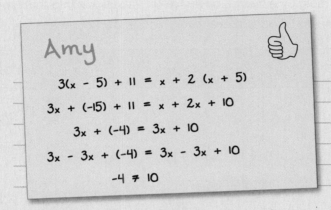

Amy

$3(x - 5) + 11 = x + 2(x + 5)$

$3x + (-15) + 11 = x + 2x + 10$

$3x + (-4) = 3x + 10$

$3x - 3x + (-4) = 3x - 3x + 10$

$-4 \neq 10$

What happened to the term with the variable?

What did Damon do differently?

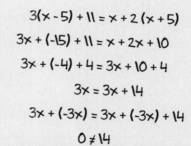

Damon

$3(x - 5) + 11 = x + 2(x + 5)$

$3x + (-15) + 11 = x + 2x + 10$

$3x + (-4) + 4 = 3x + 10 + 4$

$3x = 3x + 14$

$3x + (-3x) = 3x + (-3x) + 14$

$0 \neq 14$

1. Explain why both Amy's and Damon's methods are correct, but have different solutions.

2. How would you interpret the final equation in each solution? Is the final equation always true, sometimes true, or never true? Explain your reasoning.

3. Complete the table by substituting the given values of x into the expressions from each side of the equation and evaluate them. Show your work.

x	$3(x - 5) + 11$	$x + 2(x + 5)$
−4		
−2		
1		
5		

4. Based on the results of evaluating each row, does it appear that the expressions are equivalent based on the values in the table? Explain your reasoning.

5. Graph each expression on your graphing calculator and sketch each graph on the coordinate plane shown.

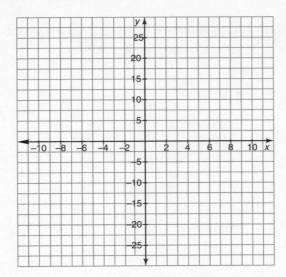

Can you predict how the graph will look?

6. What do you notice about each graph? What does this mean in terms of a value of x for which these expressions are equivalent?

7. Damon says, "Since the graphs never intersect, there are no solutions to this equation." Is Damon correct? Explain your reasoning.

Talk the Talk

1. Solve each equation and determine if there are no solutions, one solution, or an infinite number of solutions. Check your answers.

a. $2x - 7 + 3x = 4x + 2$

b. $3(x - 1) + x = 4(x + 2)$

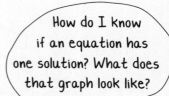

How do I know if an equation has one solution? What does that graph look like?

c. $5(2x - 1) + x + 17 = 5x + 6(x + 2)$

2. When you solve any equation, describe how you know when there will be:

    a. one solution.

    b. no solution.

    c. infinitely many solutions.

3. When you use a graphing calculator and you graph the left side of an equation as y_1 and the right side of the same equation as y_2, describe what the display will look like if there is:

    a. one solution.

    b. no solution.

    c. infinitely many solutions.

 Be prepared to share your solutions and methods.

1

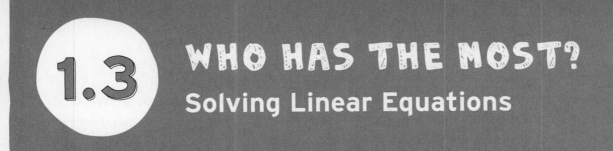

Learning Goal

In this lesson, you will:

▶ Write and solve linear equations.

A magic square is an arrangement of numbers such that the sum of the numbers in each row and each column is the same.

A magic square has *n* rows and *n* columns. For example, the magic square shown has 3 rows and 3 columns.

1	5	9
8	3	4
6	7	2

This magic square is special. It is called a *normal* magic square because it contains each counting number from 1 to n^2. That is, it contains each counting number from 1 to 3^2, or 1 to 9.

There is an equation you can use to determine the sum of each row and column in a normal magic square. It is $s = \dfrac{n(n^2 + 1)}{2}$, where *s* stands for the sum.

Can you create a 4 × 4 normal magic square? What is the sum of each row and column in a 4 × 4 normal magic square?

Problem 1 How Many DVDs Do I Have?

Sometimes, you are asked to determine the value of unknown quantities using only information you have for a quantity. For example, inventory managers can determine how much product was sold and how much product to order using algebraic equations.

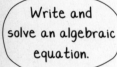

Five friends have a certain number of DVDs.

- Dan has the fewest.
- Donna has 7 more than Dan.
- Betty has twice as many as Donna.
- Jerry has 3 times as many as Dan.
- Kenesha has 6 less than Donna.

1. Define a variable for the number of DVDs that Dan has.

> Think about how the numbers of DVDs compare among the friends.

2. Use your defined variable to write algebraic expressions to represent the number of DVDs each person has.

   a. DVDs that Donna owns:

   b. DVDs that Betty owns:

   c. DVDs that Jerry owns:

   d. DVDs that Kenesha owns:

> Write and solve an algebraic equation.

3. If the friends have a total of 182 DVDs altogether, then how many does each person have? Make sure to check your work.

   a. DVDs that Dan owns: b. DVDs that Donna owns:

   c. DVDs that Betty owns: d. DVDs that Jerry owns:

   e. DVDs that Kenesha owns:

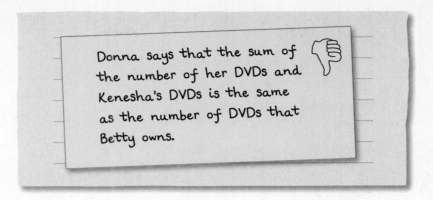

Donna says that the sum of the number of her DVDs and Kenesha's DVDs is the same as the number of DVDs that Betty owns.

4. Write and solve an algebraic equation to show why Donna's reasoning is incorrect.

Problem 2   Raising Money!

A group of club members raised money for a club trip.

- Henry raised $7.50 less than Harry.

- Helen raised twice as much as Henry.

- Heddy raised a third as much as Helen.

- Hailey raised $4 less than 3 times as much as Helen.

1. Define a variable for the amount of money Harry raised.

Read each comparison carefully and don't forget to use parentheses to represent quantities.

2. Use your defined variable to write algebraic expressions to represent the amount each person raised.

   a. The amount of money Henry raised:

   b. The amount of money Helen raised:

   c. The amount of money Heddy raised:

   d. The amount of money Hailey raised:

3. If Harry raised $55, how much money did each person raise?

   a. The amount of money Henry raised:

   b. The amount of money Helen raised:

   c. The amount of money Heddy raised:

   d. The amount of money Hailey raised:

4. If Heddy raised $40, how much money did each person raise?

Since you know how much money Heddy raised, who should you consider next?

a. The amount of money Harry raised:

b. The amount of money Henry raised:

c. The amount of money Helen raised:

d. The amount of money Hailey raised:

5. If Henry, Helen, and Hailey raised $828.50 altogether, how much money did each person raise?

a. The amount of money Harry raised:

b. The amount of money Henry raised:

c. The amount of money Helen raised:

d. The amount of money Heddy raised:

e. The amount of money Hailey raised:

6. Could Harry and Henry together have raised the same amount of money as Helen? Explain your reasoning.

7. If Heddy and Hailey raised $126 altogether, how much money did each person raise?

    a. The amount of money Harry raised:

    b. The amount of money Henry raised:

    c. The amount of money Helen raised:

    d. The amount of money Heddy raised:

    e. The amount of money Hailey raised:

 Be prepared to share your solutions and methods.

1.4 GAMES AND PRACTICE
Solving More Linear Equations

1

Learning Goal

In this lesson, you will:

▶ Solve linear equations.

Y ou probably have played your share of games. You either have played games in a sports setting, or perhaps you played board games or video games. However, game playing isn't something that is a new invention. In fact, throughout history people have enjoyed playing games. For example, many experts feel that the oldest board game originated from Egypt in approximately 3500 B.C. And games go beyond just board games. Another type of game people have loved to participate in is solving riddles.

To solve riddles, it takes using the information known to determine the information that is unknown. Have you ever tried solving riddles? What strategies have you used to solve riddles?

Problem 1   How Many MP3s Do I Have?

Terry, Trudy, Tom, and Trevor have challenged their friends with this riddle.

- Terry said: "If you add 150 to the number of MP3 downloads Tom has and then double that number and finally divide it by three, you have the number of MP3 downloads I have."

- Trudy said: "If you take the number of MP3 downloads Tom has, subtract 30, multiply that difference by 5, and finally divide that product by 4, the result will be the number of MP3 downloads I have."

- Trevor said: "Well, if you take twice the number of MP3 downloads Tom has, add 30, multiply the sum by 4, and finally divide that product by 3, you will have the number of MP3 downloads I have."

1. Do you have enough information to determine how many MP3 downloads each person has?

2. What do you need to know to determine the number of MP3 downloads each person has?

3. Define a variable for the number of MP3 downloads Tom has, and then write expressions for the number each of the other people has.

   a. The number of MP3 downloads Terry has:

   b. The number of MP3 downloads Trudy has:

   c. The number of MP3 downloads Trevor has:

4. Suppose Tom has 150 MP3 downloads. Determine how many MP3 downloads each person has.

   a. Terry

   b. Trudy

   c. Trevor

5. What if Terry and Trevor have the same number of MP3 downloads? How many MP3 downloads would each person have?

   a. The number of MP3 downloads Tom has:

   b. The number of MP3 downloads Trudy has:

   c. The number of MP3 downloads Trevor and Terry have:

6. What if the sum of Trudy's and Trevor's MP3 downloads is 39 more than the number Terry has? How many would each person have?

a. The number of MP3 downloads Tom has:

b. The number of MP3 downloads Trudy has:

c. The number of MP3 downloads Trevor has:

d. The number of MP3 downloads Terry has:

Problem 2   Practice

Solve each equation shown. Make sure to check your work.

1. $\frac{3}{4}(2x + 5) = 14$

2. $\frac{-7(3x + 6)}{3} = 7$

Pay close attention to the sign of numbers especially when using the Distributive Property.

3. $\dfrac{-3(-2x - 5)}{4} = -5(3x + 5) + \dfrac{5}{4}$

4. $\dfrac{2}{3}(6x - 5) = 2 - \dfrac{1}{3}(3x - 2)$

 Be prepared to share your solutions and methods.

Chapter 1   Summary

Key Terms

▶ two-step equation (1.1)

▶ inverse operations (1.1)

▶ solution (1.1)

▶ coefficient (1.1)

▶ constant (1.1)

▶ Properties of Equality (1.1)

1.1 Solving Two-Step Equations

Many situations can be modeled by equations that need more than one operation to solve. Perform inverse operations to get the variable by itself on one side of the equals sign to solve the equation.

Example

Follow the steps of inverse operations to calculate the solution for the equation
$6x + 9 = 33$

$$6x + 9 = 33$$
$$6x + 9 - 9 = 33 - 9$$
$$6x = 24$$
$$\frac{6x}{6} = \frac{24}{6}$$
$$x = 4$$

Great job on your first chapter of Course 3! Remember a good attitude and hard work will lead to your success this year.

1.2 Solving Equations That Have Infinite Solutions

When solving an equation with infinite solutions, the final equation after simplifying is always true for any value of the variable.

Example

The equation shown has infinite solutions because the constants are equivalent to each other.

$$2(x-3) + x - 5 = 4(x-5) + 9 - x$$
$$2x + (-6) + x + (-5) = 4x + (-20) + 9 + (-x)$$
$$2x + x + (-6) + (-5) = 4x + (-x) + (-20) + 9$$
$$3x + (-11) = 3x + (-11)$$
$$3x + (-3x) + (-11) = 3x + (-3x) + (-11)$$
$$-11 = -11$$

1.2 Solving Equations That Have No Solutions

When solving an equation that has no solutions, the final equation after simplifying is never true for any value of the variable.

Example

The equation shown has no solutions because the two constants are not equivalent to each other.

$$6(2x+3) - x = 5(3x-2) - 4x + 1$$
$$12x + 18 + (-x) = 15x + (-10) + (-4x) + 1$$
$$12x + (-x) + 18 = 15x + (-4x) + (-10) + 1$$
$$11x + 18 = 11x + (-9)$$
$$11x + (-11x) + 18 = 11x + (-11x) + (-9)$$
$$18 \neq -9$$

1.3 Writing and Solving Linear Equations

Define a variable and use the variable to write algebraic expressions to represent the different amounts in the problem situation. Combine the expressions to write and solve an algebraic equation.

Example

The ages of four siblings equals 27. Let x represent Paige's age.

- Peter is 2 years older than Paige: $x + 2$

- Perry is 3 years older than twice Paige's age: $2x + 3$

- Pippa is 11 years younger than Perry: $(2x + 3) - 11$

$$x + (x + 2) + (2x + 3) + [(2x+3) - 11] = 27$$
$$x + x + 2x + 2x + 2 + 3 + 3 + (-11) = 27$$
$$6x + (-3) = 27$$
$$6x + (-3) + 3 = 27 + 3$$
$$6x = 30$$
$$\frac{6x}{6} = \frac{30}{6}$$
$$x = 5$$

Paige = 5
Peter = 5 + 2, or 7
Perry = 2(5) + 3; or 13
Pippa = 2(5) + 3 − 11, or 2

Solving Linear Equations

Combine terms and perform inverse operations to get the variable by itself on one side of the equals sign to solve the equation. Check your solution by substituting the solution for the variable in the original equation.

Example

You must perform operations and inverse operations to determine the value of the variable. Once the variable's value is determined, the value is substituted into the original equation.

$$\frac{2(-4x - 6)}{5} = \frac{7}{15}(3x + 9) - \frac{3}{5}$$

$$5\left(\frac{2(-4x - 6)}{5}\right) = 5\left(\frac{7}{15}(3x + 9) - \frac{3}{5}\right)$$

$$2(-4x - 6) = \frac{7}{3}(3x + 9) - 3$$

$$-8x - 12 = 7x + 21 - 3$$

$$-8x - 12 - 18 = 7x + 18 - 18$$

$$-8x + 8x - 30 = 7x + 8x$$

$$-30 = 15x$$

$$\frac{-30}{15} = \frac{15x}{15}$$

$$-2 = x$$

Check:

$$\frac{2(-4(-2)-6)}{5} \overset{?}{=} \frac{7}{15}(3(-2) + 9) - \frac{3}{5}$$

$$\frac{2(8-6)}{5} \overset{?}{=} \frac{7}{15}(-6 + 9) - \frac{3}{5}$$

$$\frac{4}{5} \overset{?}{=} \frac{7}{5} - \frac{3}{5}$$

$$\frac{4}{5} = \frac{4}{5}$$

2 LINEAR FUNCTIONS

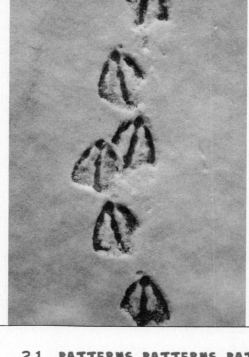

Animal trackers are experts at identifying animals by their footprints. From tracks they can also sometimes tell what direction the animal was heading, the age of the animal, and even if it is male or female! Can you guess what animal made the tracks shown in the picture?

2.1 PATTERNS, PATTERNS, PATTERNS...

Developing Sequences of Numbers from Diagrams and Contexts

Learning Goals

In this lesson, you will:

▶ Write sequences of numbers generated from the creation of diagrams and written contexts.

▶ State varying growth patterns of sequences.

Key Terms

▶ sequence

▶ term

▶ ellipsis

Legend tells us that when the inventor of the game of chess showed his work to the emperor, the emperor was so pleased that he allowed the inventor to choose any prize he wished. So the very wise inventor asked for the following: 1 gold coin for the first square on the chess board, 2 gold coins for the second square, 4 coins for the third, and so on up to the 64th square. The emperor, not as wise as the inventor, quickly agreed to such a cheap prize. Unfortunately, the emperor could not afford to pay even the amount for just the 32nd square: 4,294,967,295 gold coins!

How many gold coins would the emperor have to pay for just the 10th square? 20th square? What pattern did you use to calculate your answers?

Problem 1 Sequences

The inventor from the story used his knowledge of *sequences* to his advantage to gain riches.

A **sequence** is a pattern involving an ordered arrangement of numbers, geometric figures, letters, or other objects. A **term** in a sequence is an individual number, figure, or letter in the sequence.

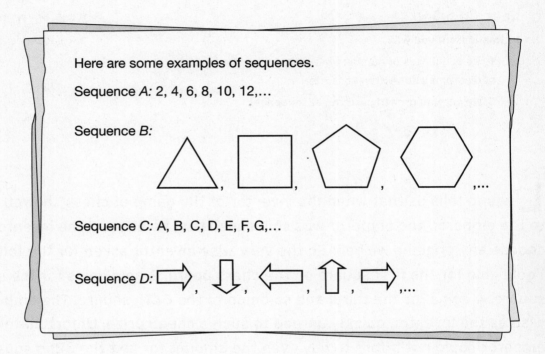

Here are some examples of sequences.

Sequence *A:* 2, 4, 6, 8, 10, 12,...

Sequence *B:*

Sequence *C:* A, B, C, D, E, F, G,...

Sequence *D:*

Often, only the first few terms of a sequence are listed, followed by an *ellipsis*. An **ellipsis** is three periods, which stand for "and so on."

1. What is the next term in Sequence *A*?

2. What is the third term in Sequence *B*?

3. What is the twenty-fifth term in Sequence *C*?

4. What is the twelfth term in Sequence *D*?

Problem 2   Designing a Bead Necklace

Emily is designing a necklace by alternating black and green beads. To create her necklace, she performs the following steps.

Step 1:   She starts with one black bead.

Step 2:   Next, she places one green bead on each side of the black bead.

Step 3:   Then, she places two black beads on each side of the green beads.

Step 4:   Then, she places three green beads on each side of the black beads.

Step 5 and 6:   She continues this pattern two more times, alternating between black and green sets of beads.

1. Write the first six terms in the sequence that represents this situation. Make sure each term indicates the total number of beads on the necklace after Emily completes that step. Finally, explain how you determined the sequence.

If you need help, draw the sequence on the necklace.

Problem 3 Crafting Toothpick Houses

Ross is crafting toothpick houses for the background of a diorama. He creates one house and then adds additional houses by adjoining them as shown.

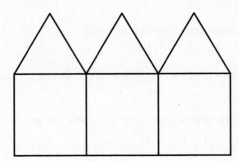

A diorama is a three-dimensional natural scene in which models of people, animals, or plants are seen against a background.

1. Write the first eight terms in the sequence that represents this situation. The first term should indicate the number of toothpicks used for one house. The second term should indicate the total number of toothpicks needed for two houses, and so on. Explain your reasoning.

2. How is the number of toothpicks needed to build each house represented in the sequence?

Problem 4   Taking Apart a Card Trick

Matthew is performing a card trick. It is important that he collect the cards shown in a particular order. Each turn, he collects all of the cards in the right-most column, and all the cards in the bottom row.

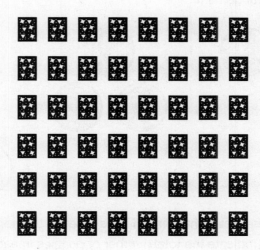

1. Write a sequence to show the number of cards removed during each of the first five turns.

2. Write a sequence to show the number of cards remaining after each of the first five turns.

3. What pattern is shown in each sequence?

Problem 5   Arranging Pennies

Lenny is making arrangements with pennies. He has made three penny arrangements and now he wants to make five more arrangements. Each time he adds another arrangement, he needs to add one more row to the base than the previous row in the previous arrangement.

1. Write the first eight terms in the sequence that represents this situation. Each term should indicate the total number of pennies in each arrangement.
   Explain your reasoning.

2. Explain why the pattern does not increase by the same amount each time.

Problem 6 Building Stairs

Dawson is stacking cubes in configurations that look like stairs. Each new configuration has one additional step.

A configuration is another way of saying an arrangement of things.

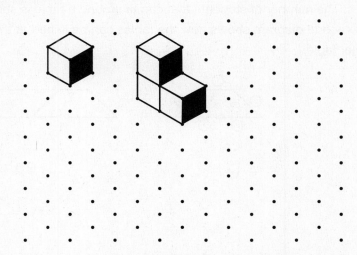

1. Write the first five terms in the sequence that represents this situation. Each term should indicate the number of faces shown from the cubes shown. The bottom faces are not shown. The first cube has 5 shown faces. Explain your reasoning.

2. Predict the number of shown faces in a stair configuration that is 7 cubes high. Show your work.

Problem 7   Arranging Classroom Tables

Some schools purchase classroom tables that have trapezoid-shaped tops rather than rectangular tops. The tables fit together nicely to arrange the classroom in a variety of ways. The number of students that can fit around a table is shown in the first diagram. The second diagram shows how the tables can be joined at the sides to make one longer table.

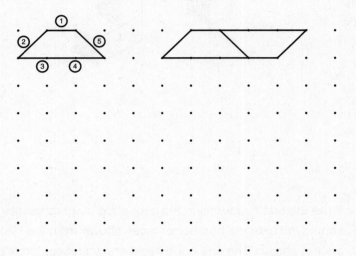

1. Write the first 5 terms in the sequence that represents this situation. Each term should indicate the total number of students that can sit around one, two, three, four, and five tables. Explain your reasoning.

2. The first trapezoid table seats five students. Explain why each additional table does not have seats for five students.

Problem 8   Drawing Flower Petals

Draw a flower in a series of stages. The figure shows a pair of flower petals as the starting point, Stage 0. In each stage, draw new petal pairs in the middle of every petal pair already drawn.

● In Stage 1, you will draw _____ petals.

● In Stage 2, you will draw _____ petals.

● In Stage 3, you will draw _____ petals.

1. Write the first 5 terms in the sequence that represents this situation. Each term should indicate the number of new petals drawn in that stage. Explain your reasoning.

There are all kinds of sequences!

Problem 9   Babysitting

Every Friday, Sarah earns $14 for babysitting. Every Saturday, Sarah spends $10 going out with her friends.

1. Write a sequence to show the amounts of money Sarah has every Friday after babysitting and every Saturday after going out with her friends for five consecutive weeks. The sequence should have 10 terms. Explain your reasoning.

Problem 10   Recycling

The first week of school, Ms. Sinopoli asked her class to participate in collecting cans for recycling. The students started bringing in cans the second week of school. They collected 120 cans per week.

1. Write a sequence to show the running total of cans collected through the first nine weeks of school. Explain your reasoning.

Problem 11   Selling Tickets

Sam is working at the ticket booth during a basketball game. His cash box has two $10 bills, five $5 bills, and twenty $1 bills. Tickets cost $3.

1. How much money does Sam have at the beginning of the basketball game?

2. Write a sequence to show the amount of cash Sam has available to start selling tickets, and the amounts available after selling one ticket, two tickets, three tickets, four tickets, and five tickets. Explain your reasoning.

Talk the Talk

There are many different patterns that can generate a sequence. Some possible patterns are:

- adding or subtracting by the same number each time,
- multiplying or dividing by the same number each time,
- adding by a different number each time, with the numbers being part of a pattern,
- alternating between adding and subtracting.

The next term in a sequence is calculated by determining the pattern of the sequence and then using that pattern on the last known term of the sequence.

Look back at Problems 2 through 11.

1. Describe the pattern of each sequence by completing the table shown.

Sequence Name	Increases or Decreases	Describe the Pattern
Designing a Bead Necklace		
Crafting a Toothpick House		
Taking Apart a Card Trick (1)		
Arranging Pennies		
Building Stairs		
Arranging Classroom Tables		
Drawing Flower Petals		
Babysitting		
Recycling		
Selling Tickets		

2. Which sequences are similar? Explain your reasoning.

 Be prepared to share your solutions and methods.

EVERY GRAPH TELLS A STORY
2.2
Describing Characteristics of Graphs

Learning Goals

In this lesson, you will:

▶ Describe characteristics of graphs using mathematical terminology.

▶ Describe a real-world situation that could be represented by a given graph.

Key Terms

▶ discrete graph
▶ continuous graph
▶ linear graph
▶ collinear points
▶ non-linear graph

Have you ever followed a trail of animal tracks? For expert animal trackers, there are many more signs to look for instead of just paw prints. Expert trackers look for rub, like when a deer scrapes velvet off its antlers. They look for chews—where a twig or section of grass has been eaten. If there is a clean cut on the plant, it may likely have been caused by an animal with incisors (like a rodent). If the plants have teeth marks all over them, those plants may likely have been eaten by a predator.

And of course, trackers look for scat, or droppings. From scat, trackers can tell an animal's shape and size and what the animal eats. Tubular scat may come from raccoons, bears, and skunks. Teardrop-shaped scat may come from an animal in the cat family. How do you follow clues in mathematics to solve problems?

Incisors are the sharp teeth in humans and animals!

Problem 1 Characteristics of Graphs

There are many ways that data can be represented through graphical displays. In this lesson, you will explore many characteristics of graphs.

1. Graph the first four terms of Sequence *A*: 0, 2, 4, 6. Let the term number represent the *x*-coordinate, and let the term value represent the *y*-coordinate. Then, list the coordinates of the points on your graph.

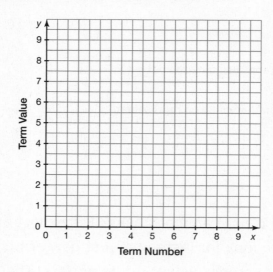

Note that the term value is the number itself. The term number indicates where the term falls in the sequence (1st, 2nd, 3rd, and so on).

2. Would it make sense to connect the points on your graph? Why or why not?

A **discrete graph** is a graph of isolated points. Often, those points are counting numbers and do not consist of fractional numbers. A **continuous graph** is a graph with no breaks in it. The points in a continuous graph can have whole numbers and fractions to represent data points.

3. Is your graph from Question 1 discrete or continuous? Explain your reasoning.

Time to get out your scissors.

4. Are the graphs of any sequence discrete or continuous? Explain your reasoning.

5. Carefully cut out Graphs *A* through *L* on the following pages.

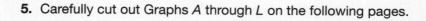

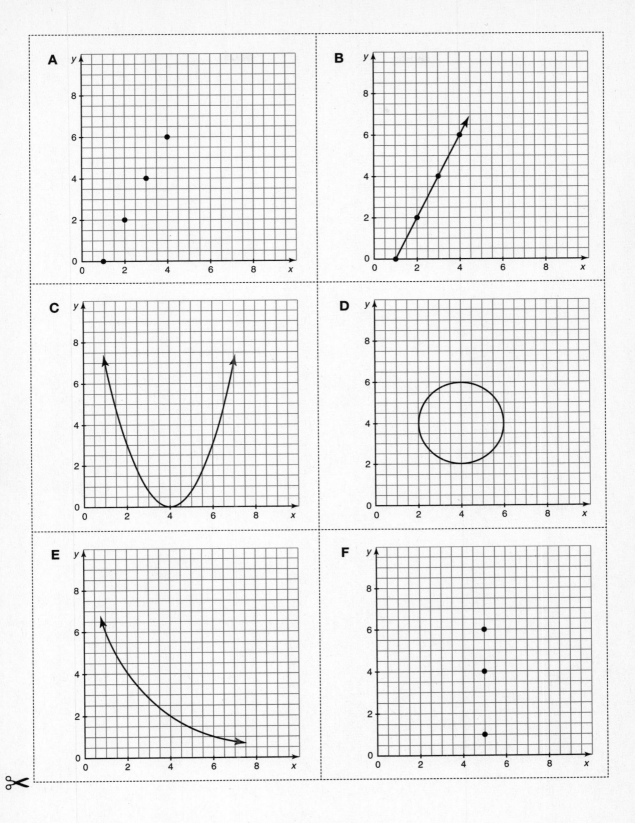

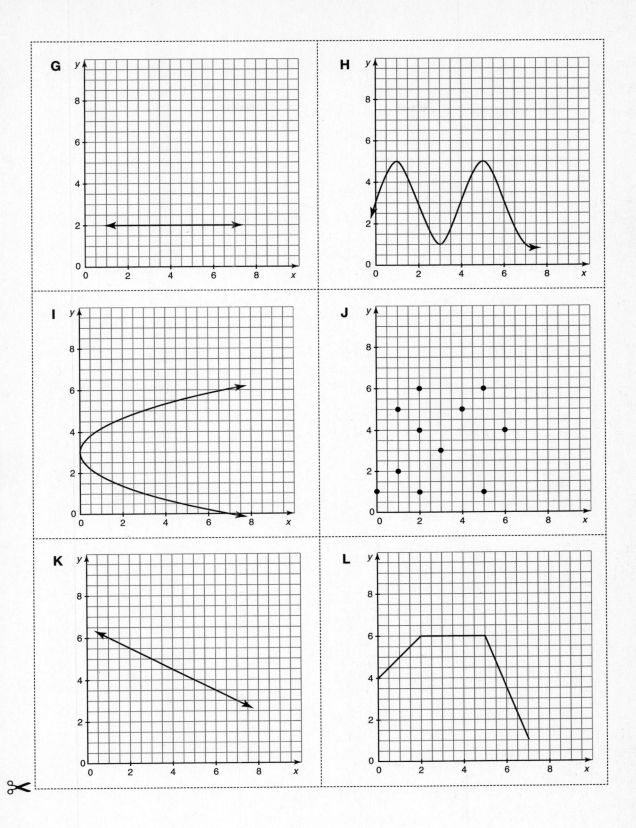

2

6. Determine if the graphs you cut out are discrete or continuous.

   a. Sort the graphs into two groups: those graphs that are discrete and those graphs that are continuous.

   b. Record your findings in the table by writing the letter of each graph.

Discrete Graphs	Continuous Graphs

7. Determine if the graphs are increasing, decreasing, both increasing and decreasing, or neither increasing nor decreasing.

   a. Analyze each graph from left to right.

   b. Sort the graphs into four groups: those that are increasing, those that are decreasing, those that are both increasing and decreasing, and those that are neither increasing nor decreasing.

   c. Record your findings in the table by writing the letter of each graph.

Increasing	Decreasing	Both Increasing and Decreasing	Neither Increasing nor Decreasing

A **linear graph** is a graph that is a line or a series of *collinear points*. **Collinear points** are points that lie in the same straight line. A **non-linear graph** is a graph that is not a line and therefore not a series of collinear points.

8. Determine whether Graphs *A–L* are linear or non-linear graphs.

   a. Sort the graphs into two groups: those that are linear and those that are non-linear.

   b. Record your findings in the table by writing the letter of each graph.

Linear Graph	Non-linear Graph

9. Clip Graphs *A–L* together, and keep them for Lessons 2 and 3.

You will use these graphs in another lesson. So, put them in a safe place.

Problem 2   Making Sense of Graphs

The graph shown represents Greg's distance from home after driving for *x* hours.

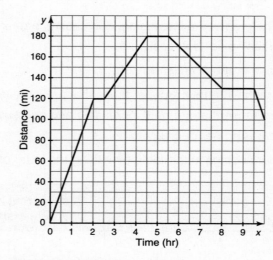

How can you tell by looking at the graph when Greg was traveling the fastest?

1. Analyze the graph between 0 and 2 hours.

   a. How far from home was Greg after driving for 2 hours?

   b. How fast did Greg drive during this time? Explain your reasoning.

   c. How do you know that Greg traveled at the same rate for the first two hours? Describe in terms of the graph.

2. Analyze the graph between 2 and 2.5 hours.

   a. How far did Greg travel from home between 2 and 2.5 hours?

b. How fast did he travel during this time? Explain your reasoning.

c. Describe the shape of the graph between 2 and 2.5 hours.

3. Complete the table.

Label each segment of the graph with letters *A* through *G*, beginning from the left. Record the time interval for each segment. Then, describe what happened in the problem situation represented by that segment of the graph. State how fast Greg traveled and in what direction (either from home or to home).

Segment	Time Interval (hours)	Description of Greg's Trip
A	0 to 2	Greg traveled 120 miles from home at a rate of 60 mph.
B	2 to 2.5	Greg took a half-hour break when he was 120 miles from home.
C		
D		
E		
F		
G		

4. The crew at the community swimming pool prepared the pool for opening day. The graph shows the depth of water in the swimming pool after x hours.

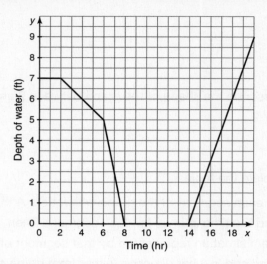

a. Why do you think the pool was emptied and then refilled?

b. Complete the table.

Label each segment of the graph with letters A through E, beginning from the left. Record the time interval for each segment. Then, describe what occurred in the problem situation represented by that segment in the graph. State how fast the water level in the pool changed and whether it was being drained or filled.

Segment	Time Interval (hours)	Description of the Water in the Pool
A		
B		
C		
D		
E		

c. Was the pool being emptied at the same rate the entire time? Explain using mathematics and the graph.

d. Why does it make sense for the graph of this situation to be continuous rather than discrete?

Problem 3   Tell a Story

You and a friend go to the movies and decide to share a large bucket of popcorn. Write a story to describe each graph.

1.

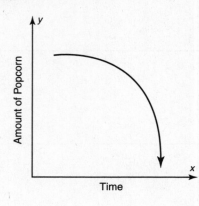

As time increases, what happens to the amount of popcorn?

2.

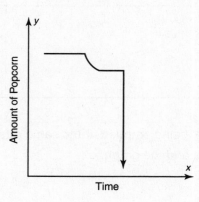

Be prepared to share your solutions and methods.

TO BE OR NOT TO BE A FUNCTION?

Defining and Recognizing Functions

2.3

Learning Goals

In this lesson, you will:

▶ Define relation and function.

▶ Determine whether a relation (represented as a mapping, set of ordered pairs, table, sequence, graph, equation, or context) is a function.

Key Terms

▶ mapping

▶ set

▶ relation

▶ input

▶ output

▶ function

▶ domain

▶ range

▶ scatter plot

▶ vertical line test

In September 2009, museum volunteers in England began work on restoring the WITCH machine—regarded as the first modern computer still able to work. This huge computer, as long as an entire wall in a large room, was built starting in 1949 and was functional until 1957.

WITCH was used to perform mathematical calculations, but instead of typed input, the computer had to be fed paper tape for inputs. Then, the computer would produce its output on paper as well. Even though it was so huge, WITCH could only perform calculations as fast as a human with a modern calculator.

What types of inputs and outputs do modern computers use and produce? How does a modern computer turn inputs into outputs?

Problem 1   Analyzing Ordered Pairs

As you learned previously, ordered pairs consist of an *x*-coordinate and a *y*-coordinate. You also learned that a series of ordered pairs on a coordinate plane can represent a pattern. You can also use a *mapping* to show ordered pairs. **Mapping** represents two sets of objects or items. An arrow connects the items together to represent a relationship between the two items.

1. Write the set of ordered pairs that represent a relationship in each mapping.

   a.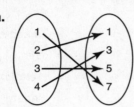

   b.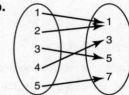

Use brackets, { }, to denote a set.

   c.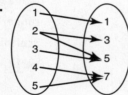

   d.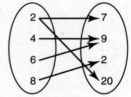

2. Create a mapping from the set of ordered pairs.

   a. {(5, 8), (11, 9), (6, 8), (8, 5)}

   b. {(3, 4), (9, 8), (3, 7), (4, 20)}

When you write out the ordered pairs for a mapping, you are writing a *set* of ordered pairs. A **set** is a collection of numbers, geometric figures, letters, or other objects that have some characteristic in common.

3. Write the set of ordered pairs to represent each table.

a.

Input	Output
−10	20
−5	10
0	0
5	10
10	20

b.

x	y
20	−10
10	−5
0	0
10	5
20	10

The mappings or ordered pairs shown in Questions 1 through 3 form *relations*. A **relation** is any set of ordered pairs or the mapping between a set of *inputs* and a set of *outputs*. The first coordinate of an ordered pair in a relation is the **input**, and the second coordinate is the **output**. A **function** maps each input to one and only one output. In other words, a function has no input with more than one output. The **domain** of a function is the set of all inputs of the function. The **range** of a function is the set of all outputs of the function.

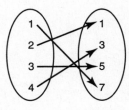

In the mapping shown the domain is {1, 2, 3, 4} and the range is {1, 3, 5, 7}.

This mapping represents a function because each input, or domain value, is mapped to only one output, or range value.

Notice the use of set notation when writing the domain and range.

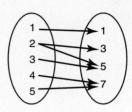

In the mapping shown the domain is {1, 2, 3, 4, 5} and the range is {1, 3, 5, 7}.

This mapping does not represent a function.

4. State why the relation in the example shown is not a function.

5. State the domain and range for each relation in Questions 2 and 3. Then, determine which relations represent functions. If the relation is not a function, state why not.

6. Review and analyze Emil's work.

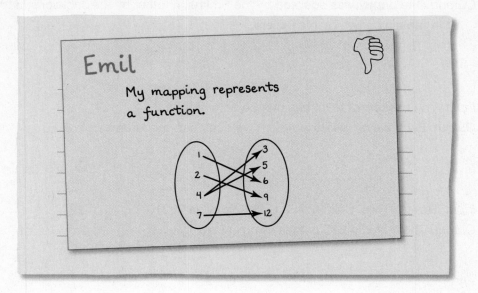

Explain why Emil's mapping is not an example of a function.

Problem 2   Analyzing Contexts

Read each context and decide whether it fits the definition of a function.
Explain your reasoning.

1. *Input:* Sue writes a thank-you note to her best friend.
Output: Her best friend receives the thank-you note in the mail.

2. *Input:* A football game is being telecast.
Output: It appears on televisions in millions of homes.

3. *Input:* There are four puppies in a litter.

   Output: One puppy was adopted by the Smiths, another by the Jacksons, and the remaining two by the Fullers.

4. *Input:* The basketball team has numbered uniforms.

   Output: Each player wears a uniform with her assigned number.

5. *Input:* Beverly Hills, California, has the zip code 90210.

   Output: There are 34,675 people living in Beverly Hills.

6. *Input:* A sneak preview of a new movie is being shown in a local theater.

   Output: 65 people are in the audience.

7. *Input:* Tara works at a fast food restaurant on weekdays and a card store on weekends.

   Output: Tara's job on any one day.

8. *Input:* Janelle sends a text message to everyone in her contact list on her cell phone.

   Output: There are 41 friends and family on Janelle's contact list.

9. Create your own context problem, and decide whether it represents a function. Trade with a partner, and solve your partner's problem. Then, discuss your responses.

   Input:

   Output:

Problem 3   Analyzing Sequences

1. Determine if each sequence represents a function. Explain why or why not. If it is a function, identify its domain and range.

   a. 2, 4, 6, 8, 10, …

Remember a sequence has a term number and a term value.

Think about the mappings as ordered pairs.

   b. 1, 0, 1, 0, 1, …

   c. 0, 5, 10, 15, 20, …

2. What do you notice about each answer in Question 1? What conclusion can you make about sequences?

Problem 4 Analyzing Graphs

A relation can be represented as a graph. Graphs *A–L* from Lesson 2.2 provide examples of graphical representations of relations.

A **scatter plot** is a graph of a collection of ordered pairs that allows an exploration of the relationship between the points.

1. Determine if these scatter plots represent functions. Explain your reasoning.

    a.
    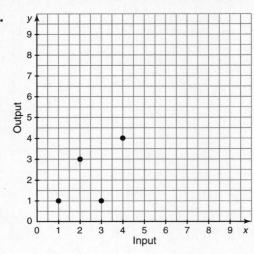

Keep in mind, a function maps each input to one and only one output.

    b.
    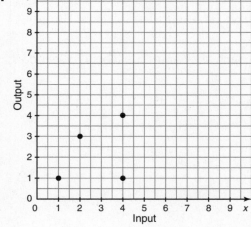

The **vertical line test** is a visual method used to determine whether a relation represented as a graph is a function. To apply the vertical line test, consider all of the vertical lines that could be drawn on the graph of a relation. If any of the vertical lines intersect the graph of the relation at more than one point, then the relation is not a function.

Review the scatter plot shown.

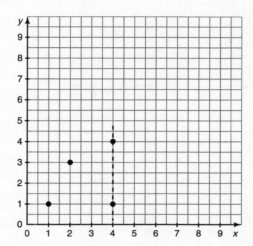

In this scatter plot, the relation is not a function. The input value 4 can be mapped to two different outputs, 1 and 4. Those two outputs are shown as intersections to the vertical line segment drawn at $x = 4$.

2. Use the vertical line test to determine if each graph represents a function. Explain your reasoning.

a.

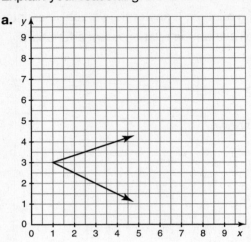

b.

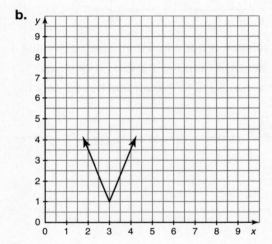

Problem 5   Analyzing Equations

So far, you have determined whether a set of data points in a scatter plot represents a function. You can also determine whether an equation is a function.

The given equation can be used to convert yards into feet. Let x represent the number of yards, and y represent the number of feet.

$$y = 3x$$

To test whether this equation is a function, first, substitute values for x into the equation, and then determine if any x-value can be mapped to more than one y-value. If each x-value has exactly one y-value, then it is a function; otherwise, it is not a function.

In this case, every x-value can be mapped to only one y-value. Each x-value is multiplied by 3. Some examples of ordered pairs are (2, 6), (10, 30), and (5, 15). So, this equation is a function.

1. Determine whether each equation is a function. List three ordered pairs that are solutions to each. Explain your reasoning.

   a. $y = 5x + 3$

   b. $y = x^2$

   c. $y = |x|$

So, if two different inputs go to the same output, that's still a function.

Time to get your graphs from the first lesson back out.

1. Sorting Activity

    a. Carefully cut out Relations *M* through *X* on the following pages.

    b. Refer to Graphs *A* through *L* from Lesson 2.

    c. Sort Relations *A* through *X* into two groups: those that are functions and those that are not functions.

    d. Record your findings in the table by writing the letter of each relation.

Functions	Not Functions

M

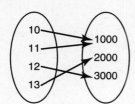

N

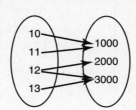

O

Input	Output
−2	4
−1	1
0	0
1	1
2	4

P

x	y
2	−4
1	−1
0	0
1	1
2	4

Q

The terms of a sequence:

7, 10, 13, 16, 19, …

R

The terms of a sequence:

10, 30, 10, 30, 10, …

2

S

The set of ordered pairs

{(2, 3), (2, 4), (2, 5),
(2, 6), (2, 7)}

T

The set of ordered pairs

{(2, 1), (3, 1), (4, 1),
(5, 1), (6, 1)}

U

$y = x^2 + 1$

V

This equation is used to calculate the number of inches in a foot:

$y = 12x$

Let x represent the number of feet and y represent the number of inches.

W

Input:
The morning announcements are read over the school intercom system during homeroom period.

Output:
All students report to homeroom at the start of the school day to listen to the announcements.

X

Input:
Each student goes through the cafeteria line.

Output:
Each student selects a lunch from the menu.

Talk the Talk

Choose the appropriate description to complete each sentence.

1. A relation is (always, sometimes, never) a function.

2. A function is (always, sometimes, never) a relation.

Be prepared to share your solutions and methods.

2.4 SCALING A CLIFF
Linear Functions

Learning Goals

In this lesson, you will:

▶ Make input-output tables for linear functions.

▶ Graph linear functions.

▶ Determine characteristics of linear functions.

Key Term

▶ linear function

Can you draw a perfectly straight line without using a ruler or other straightedge? What about over a long distance?

Carpenters and other construction workers use what is called a chalk line to mark straight lines over long distances. A chalk line tool looks a bit like a tape measure. A cord that is coated in chalk is wound inside the tool. One person pulls the cord to the end of where the line will be, and the other person holds the tool at the beginning of the line. When they have the line where they want, both people pull the cord tight, and one person pulls up on the cord and lets go so that the cord "snaps" a straight line of chalk onto the surface below the cord.

Have you ever seen or used a chalk line tool? Does anyone in your class have one they could show?

Problem 1   Climbing to the Top!

1. You and your friends are rock climbing a vertical cliff that is 108 feet tall along a beach. You have been climbing for a while and are currently 36 feet above the beach when you stop on a ledge to have a snack and then begin climbing again. You can climb about 12 feet in height each hour. If you maintain your pace after your break, how high will you have climbed in:

   a. 1 hour?

   b. 2 hours?

   c. 180 minutes?

   d. 210 minutes?

   e. Which quantities are changing? Which quantities remain constant?

   f. Which quantity depends on the other quantity?

2. Complete the table shown by first writing the name and the unit of measure for each quantity. Then, write your answers from Problem 1 in the table. Please note that you will complete the table at a later time.

To set up your labels for the table, think about what quantities are being measured and how you are counting them.

	Input	Output
Quantity Name		
Unit of Measure		
Question 1, Part (a)	1	
Question 1, Part (b)	2	
Question 1, Part (c)		
Question 1, Part (d)		
Question 5, Part (a)		84
Question 5, Part (b)		96
Question 5, Part (c)		108
Expression		

3. Define a variable for the input quantity. Enter this variable in the "Expression" row at the bottom of Column 1.

4. Write an expression that you can use to represent the output quantity in terms of the input quantity. Enter this expression in the "Expression" row under output.

5. Use your expression to write an equation that you can solve to determine each answer. Then, write your answer in the appropriate place in table.

a. How long will it be until you have climbed to 84 feet above the beach?

b. How long will it be until you have climbed to 96 feet above the beach?

c. How long will it be until you have reached the top of the cliff?

6. Create a graph to represent the values in your table. Label the horizontal axis with the input quantity and the vertical axis with the output quantity. The axes are already numbered. Finally, plot the points on the coordinate plane.

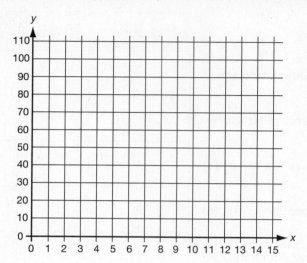

Remember, the independent quantities are always shown on the horizontal axis and the dependent quantities on the vertical axis.

7. Connect the points on your graphs.

8. Determine the domain and range of this situation.

9. Does your table represent the same domain and range? Why or why not?

10. Is the relation shown in the graph a function? Explain why or why not.

Drawing a line through the data set of a graph is a way to model or represent relationships. The points on your graph represent equivalent ratios because the climbing time per height remained constant. In some problem situations, when you draw a line all the points will make sense. In other problem situations, not all the points on the line will make sense. For example, if a graph displayed the cost per ticket, you cannot purchase a fractional part of a ticket, but the line you would draw on the graph would help you model the relationship and see how the cost changes as more tickets are purchased. So, when you graph relations and model that relationship with a line, it is up to you to consider each situation and interpret the meaning of the data values from a line drawn on a graph.

Talk the Talk

When you graph the input and output values of some functions, the graph forms a straight line. A function whose graph is a straight line is a **linear function**.

The relation shown in the graph in this lesson is a linear function. The graph is a line segment.

Let's think about the problem situation, your table, and your graph.

1. Which variable is the dependent variable?

2. Which variable is the independent variable?

3. Describe what happens to the value of the dependent variable each time the independent variable increases by 1.

4. Describe what happens to the value of the dependent variable when the independent variable increases by 2.

5. Compare the values of the dependent variable when the independent variable is 1 and 6. Describe how the dependent variable changes in relation to the independent variable.

6. Describe how the independent and dependent values change in linear functions.

 Be prepared to share your solutions and methods.

2.5

U.S. SHIRTS

Using Tables, Graphs, and Equations, Part 1

Learning Goals

In this lesson, you will:

▶ Use different models to represent a problem situation.

▶ Determine an initial value when given a final result.

▶ Identify the advantages and disadvantages of using a particular representation.

Have ever wondered where your clothes come from? Who actually makes the clothes you wear? For the most part, clothes are made in countries like Vietnam, India, Pakistan, and Mexico, just to name a few. However, only 40 to 50 years ago, clothes were created here in the United States. It was common for people to seek employment creating clothes. Well, the trend of creating clothes in the United States is slowly on the rise. The opening of boutiques and American clothes designers have stressed creating unique and cutting edge fashion, but also not to mass produce clothing—and this idea of creating clothes in the United States has reinvented itself. Why do you think clothing began being made in other countries? Do you think the United States will one day become a clothing creating powerhouse that it once was?

Problem 1 Cost Analysis

This past summer you were hired to work at a custom T-shirt shop, U.S. Shirts. One of your responsibilities is to calculate the total cost of customers' orders. The shop charges $8 per shirt plus a one-time charge of $15 to set up a T-shirt design.

1. Describe the problem situation and your responsibility in your own words.

2. What is the total cost of an order for:

   a. 3 shirts?

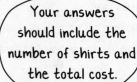

Your answers should include the number of shirts and the total cost.

If the order doubles, does the total cost double?

   b. 10 shirts?

   c. 100 shirts?

3. Explain how you calculated each total cost.

4. How many shirts can a customer buy if they have:

   a. $50 to spend?

b. $60 to spend?

What operations do you need to perform to answer each?

c. $220 to spend?

2

5. Explain how you calculated the number of shirts that each customer can buy.

6. Complete the table of values for the problem situation.

Number of Shirts Ordered	Total Cost (dollars)

7. What are the variable quantities in this problem situation? Define the variables that can represent these quantities including each quantity's units.

Variable quantities are quantities that change, and constant quantities are quantities that don't change.

8. What are the constant quantities in this problem situation? Include the units that are used to measure these quantities.

9. Which variable quantity depends on the other variable quantity?

10. Which of the variables from Question 7 is the independent variable, and which is the dependent variable?

11. Create a graph of the data from your table in Question 6 on the grid shown. First, choose your bounds and intervals by completing the table shown. Remember to label your graph clearly and name your graph.

Variable Quantity	Lower Bound	Upper Bound	Interval
Number of shirts			
Total cost			

Consider all the data values when choosing your lower and upper bounds.

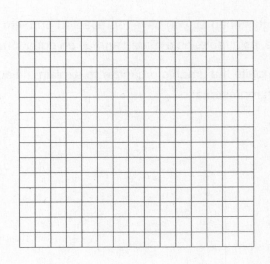

12. Draw a line to model the relationship between the number of shirts and the total cost of the shirts.

13. Do all the points on the line make sense in terms of this problem situation? Why or why not?

Use variables that make sense to you in terms of the problem situation.

14. Define the variables and write an algebraic equation for the problem situation.

15. Define the domain and range for this problem situation.

Talk the Talk

So far in this chapter, you have represented problem situations in four different ways: as a sentence, as a table, as a graph, and as an equation.

1. Complete the graphic organizer to explain the advantages and disadvantages of each representation.

Think about the type of information each representation displays.

Also think about the types of questions you can answer using each representation.

Be prepared to share your solutions and methods.

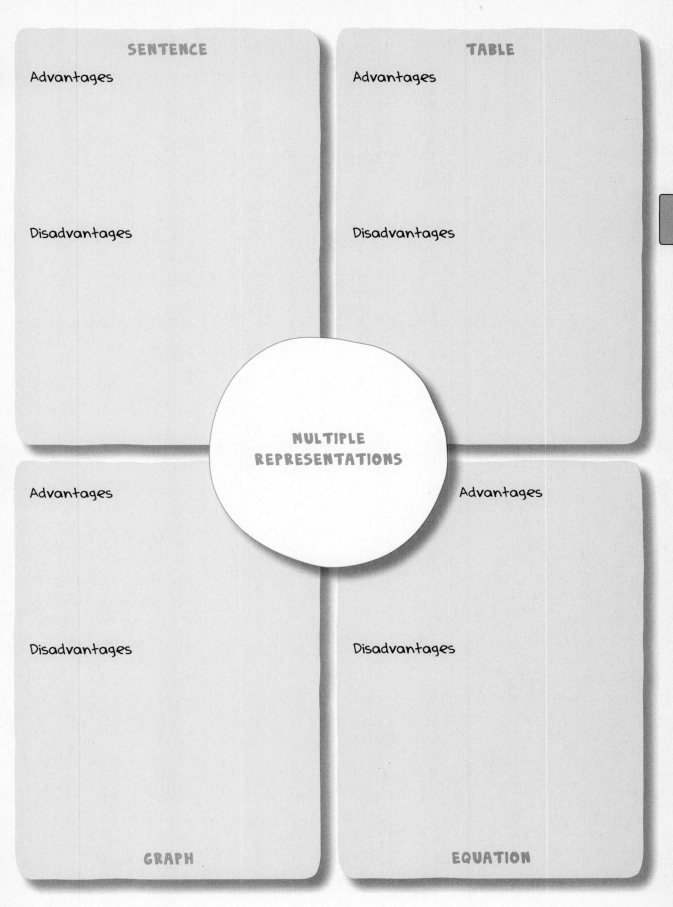

SENTENCE

Advantages

Disadvantages

TABLE

Advantages

Disadvantages

MULTIPLE
REPRESENTATIONS

Advantages

Disadvantages

GRAPH

Advantages

Disadvantages

EQUATION

2

2

HOT SHIRTS
Using Tables, Graphs, and Equations, Part 2

2.6

Learning Goals

In this lesson, you will:

▶ Use different methods to represent a problem situation.

▶ Estimate values of expressions that involve decimals.

▶ Determine an initial value when given a final result.

Key Terms

▶ estimation

▶ point of intersection

2

You might be surprised to know that the word "T-shirt" wasn't really used until the 1920s. And, until the 1950s, people thought of T-shirts as underwear. Popular actors like John Wayne and James Dean surprised audiences in the mid-1950s by wearing this underwear on screen!

Since then, T-shirts have become one of the most popular items of clothing in the world.

Problem 1 Analyzing the Competition

Previously, you explored a job at U.S. Shirts. One of U.S. Shirts' competitors, Hot Shirts, advertises that it makes custom T-shirts for $5.50 each with a one-time setup fee of $49.95. Your boss brings you the advertisement from Hot Shirts and asks you to figure out how the competition might affect business.

1. Describe the problem situation and how it will affect business in your own words.

2. What is the total customer cost of an order for:

   a. 3 shirts from Hot Shirts?

What is your initial prediction? Is Hot Shirts a strong competitor for US Shirts?

   b. 10 shirts from Hot Shirts?

   c. 50 shirts from Hot Shirts?

   d. 100 shirts from Hot Shirts?

3. Explain how you calculated the total customer costs.

Remember, you can use **estimation** to determine the approximate values before you do actual calculations to get a sense of the answer.

For example, you can estimate the difference of 125.35 and 84.95. So, you could round 125.35 down to 125, and round 84.95 up to 85. Then, calculate the difference of 125 and 85, to $125 - 85 = 40$.

You can write this as $125.35 - 84.95 \approx 40$.

The symbol $\approx$ means "is approximately equal to."

4. Estimate the value of each expression.

a. $748.75 + 60.22$

b. $345 - 214$

c. $45.13(20.44)$

5. Estimate the number of shirts that a customer can purchase from Hot Shirts for:

a. $50.

b. $60.

c. $220.

6. Explain how you used estimation to efficiently determine the number of shirts that can be purchased.

7. Complete the table of values for the problem situation.

Round to the nearest penny.

Number of Shirts Ordered	Total Cost (dollars)

8. Create a graph of the data from the table on the grid shown. First, choose your bounds and intervals by completing the table shown. Remember to label your graph clearly and name your graph.

Variable Quantity	Lower Bound	Upper Bound	Interval
Number of shirts			
Total cost			

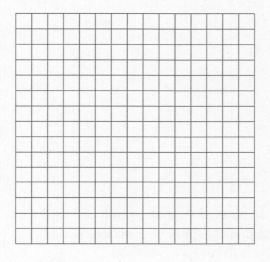

9. Define the variables and write an algebraic equation for this problem situation.

How did you define the variables in the U.S. Shirt problem?

Problem 2   Which Is the Better Buy?

You have explored the costs of ordering T-shirts from two companies, U.S. Shirts and Hot Shirts. Your boss asked you to determine which company has the better price for T-shirts in different situations.

1. Would you recommend U.S. Shirts or Hot Shirts as the better buy for an order of five or fewer T-shirts? What would each company charge for exactly five shirts? Describe how you calculated your answer.

2. For an order of 18 shirts, which company's price is the better buy? How much better is the price? Explain your reasoning.

3. For an order of 80 shirts, which company's price is better? How much better is the price? Explain your reasoning.

4. Create the graphs for the total cost for U.S. Shirts and Hot Shirts on the grid shown. First, determine the bounds and intervals for the grid by completing the table shown.

Variable Quantity	Lower Bound	Upper Bound	Interval
Number of shirts	0	150	10
Total cost	0	1500	100

Make sure you label each graph.

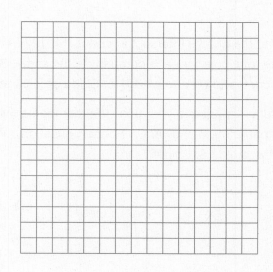

5. Estimate the number of T-shirts for which the total costs are the same. Explain how you determined the number of T-shirts.

6. For how many T-shirts is it more expensive to order from U.S. Shirts?

7. For how many T-shirts is it more expensive to order from Hot Shirts?

8. Look at your graph. Describe the graphs of the lines in your own words.

Notice that the graphs intersect at about (14, 127). This **point of intersection** indicates where the total cost for each company is the same. So, when U.S. Shirts sells 14 shirts, the total cost is $127, and when Hot Shirts sells 14 shirts, the total cost is $127.

9. Write a response to your boss that compares the costs of ordering from each company. Try to answer your boss's question, "Will Hot Shirts' prices affect the business at U.S. Shirts?"

 Be prepared to share your solutions and methods.

WHAT, NOT LINES?

2.7
Introduction to Non-Linear Functions

Learning Goals

In this lesson, you will:

▶ Define, graph, and analyze non-linear functions, including:
  - absolute value
  - area of a square
  - volume of a cube

Key Terms

▶ absolute value function
▶ square or quadratic function
▶ cube or cubic function

Have someone in your class think of a whole number from 1 to 20. Ask each other student in the class to guess what the number is. Record all the guesses without revealing the mystery number.

On the graph shown, have the recorder determine each guess on the *x*-axis and plot its distance (shown on the *y*-axis) from the mystery number.

What is the mystery number? Did you graph a function?

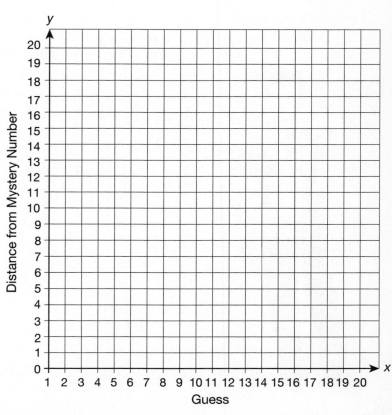

Problem 1   The V

Recall that the absolute value of a number is defined as the distance from the number to zero on a number line. The symbol for absolute value is $|x|$.

1. Evaluate each expression shown.

   a. $|-3| =$ b. $|11| =$

   c. $\left|-5\dfrac{2}{3}\right| =$ d. $|110.89| =$

2. Use the function $y = |x|$, to complete the table.

x	$y = |x|$
−7	
−3	
−1	
−0.5	
0	
2	
4	
7	

If it is stated that you are working with a function, what does that tell you about the relationship between the input and output values?

3. Graph the values from the table on the coordinate plane.

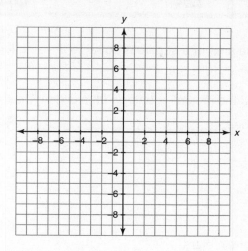

4. Connect the points to model the relationship of the equation $y = |x|$.

5. What is the domain of this function? Do all the points on the graph make sense in terms of the equation $y = |x|$. Explain your reasoning.

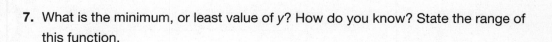

Keep in mind, the domain and range represent sets of numbers.

6. Does the graph of these points form a straight line? Explain your reasoning.

7. What is the minimum, or least value of y? How do you know? State the range of this function.

8. Is this a linear function? Explain your reasoning.

You have just graphed an *absolute value function*. An **absolute value function** is a function that can be written in the form $f(x) = |x|$, where x is any number. Function notation can be used to write functions such that the dependent variable is replaced with the name of the function, such as $f(x)$.

Problem 2   Not V but U

Recall that the area of a square is equal to the side length, s, multiplied by itself and is written as $A = s^2$.

1. Calculate the area of squares with side lengths that are:

    a. 3 inches.

    b. 5 feet.

    c. 2.4 centimeters.

    d. $12\frac{5}{8}$ inches.

In the equation $A = s^2$ the side length of a square, s, is the independent variable and the area of a square, A, is the dependent variable. This formula can also be modeled by the equation $y = x^2$, where x represents the side length of a square and y represents the area of a square.

2. Use the equation, $y = x^2$, to complete the table.

x	$y = x^2$
−3	
−2	
−1	
−0.5	
0	
2	
2.3	
3	

Does this equation represent a function?

3. Graph the values from the table on the coordinate plane.

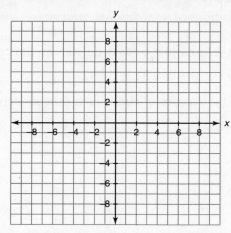

4. Connect the points to model the relationship of the equation $y = x^2$.

5. What is the domain of this function? Do all the points on the graph make sense in terms of the equation $y = x^2$. Explain your reasoning.

6. What is the minimum, or least value of y? How do you know? State the range of this function.

7. Does the graph of these points form a straight line? Explain your reasoning.

8. Is this a linear function? Explain your reasoning.

You have just graphed a *quadratic function*. A **quadratic function** is a function that can be written in the form $f(x) = ax^2 + bx + c$, where a, b, and c are any numbers and a is not equal to zero.

Problem 3   Not V or U

Recall that the volume of a cube is defined as the product of the length of one edge times itself 3 times and is written as $V = s^3$.

1. Calculate the volume of cubes with an edge length that is:

   a. 2 inches.

   b. 1.5 feet.

   c. 2.1 centimeters.

   d. $1\frac{3}{4}$ inches.

In the equation $V = s^3$, the side length of a cube, s, is the independent variable and the volume of the cube, V is the dependent variable. This formula can also be modeled by the equation $y = x^3$, where x represents the side length of a cube and y represents the volume of a cube.

2. Use the equation, $y = x^3$, to complete the table.

x	$y = x^3$
−2	
−1.5	
−1	
−0.5	
0	
1.5	
2	
2.1	

Does this equation represent a function?

3. Graph the values from the table on the coordinate plane.

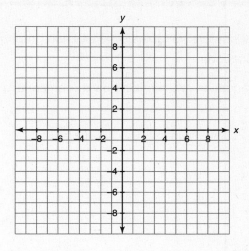

4. Connect the points to model the relationship of the equation $y = x^3$.

5. What is the domain of this function? Do all the points on the graph make sense in terms of the equation $y = x^3$. Explain your reasoning.

6. What is the minimum value of y? How do you know? State the range of this function.

7. Does the graph of these points form a straight line? Explain your reasoning.

8. Is this a linear function? Explain your reasoning.

You have just graphed a *cubic function*. A **cubic function** is a function that can be written in the form $f(x) = a_3x^3 + a_2x^2 + a_1x + a_0$.

Talk the Talk

You have just completed tables of values and graphs for three different non-linear functions.

Name each equation and explain how it represents a function.

- $y = |x|$

- $y = x^2$

- $y = x^3$

Be prepared to share your solutions and methods.

Chapter 2 Summary

Key Terms

- sequence (2.1)
- term (2.1)
- ellipsis (2.1)
- discrete graph (2.2)
- continuous graph (2.2)
- linear graph (2.2)
- collinear points (2.2)
- non-linear graph (2.2)
- mapping (2.3)

- set (2.3)
- relation (2.3)
- input (2.3)
- output (2.3)
- function (2.3)
- domain (2.3)
- range (2.3)
- scatter plot (2.3)
- vertical line test (2.3)
- linear function (2.4)

- estimation (2.6)
- point of intersection (2.6)
- absolute value function (2.7)
- square or quadratic function (2.7)
- cube or cubic function (2.7)

2.1 Writing Sequences of Numbers Generated from the Creation of Diagrams and Written Contexts

A sequence is a pattern involving an ordered arrangement of numbers, geometric figures, letters, or other objects. A term in a sequence is an individual number, figure, or letter in the sequence. Often, a diagram can be used to show how each term changes as the sequence progresses.

Example

The first three terms in this sequence show how many total squares are in each set of steps as new steps are added.

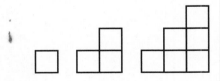

If two more figures were drawn, the sequence would be 1, 3, 6, 10, 15, with each term indicating the total number of squares in each figure.

2.1 Stating Varying Growth Patterns of Sequences

There are many different patterns that can generate a sequence of numbers. Some possible patterns are:

- adding or subtracting by the same number each time,
- multiplying or dividing by the same number each time,
- adding by a different number each time, with the numbers being part of a pattern,
- alternating between adding and subtracting.

Example

Fletcher is starting a new job delivering the newspaper. He will make $20 every Friday and will put $8 into his savings account every Monday morning. You can write a sequence for the amount of money that Fletcher earns and how much he has left after putting money in his savings.

The sequence is $0, $20, $12, $32, $24, $44, $36, $56, $48, $68. The pattern in the sequence is add 20, then subtract 8.

The human brain loves to find patterns and luckily they are everywhere— music, art, sports, nature! Can you find any patterns where you are?

2.2 Describing Characteristics of Graphs Using Mathematical Terminology

A discrete graph is a graph that consists of isolated points. A continuous graph is a graph with no breaks in it. A linear graph is a graph that is a line or a series of collinear points. A non-linear graph is a graph that is not a line and not a series of collinear points.

Example

Two different graphs are shown.

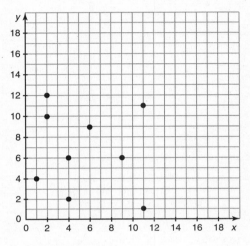

The graph is discrete, non-linear, and neither increasing nor decreasing.

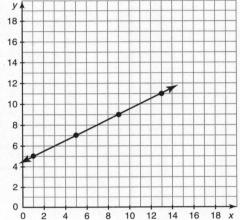

The graph is continuous, linear, and increasing.

2.2 Describing a Real World Situation Represented by a Given Graph

A variety of real-world situations can be represented by graphs.

Example

The graph shown describes a situation that could represent student math scores throughout the school year.

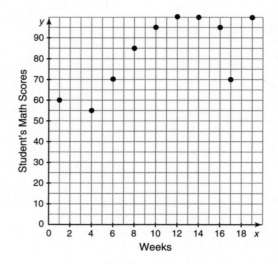

The student's math score from Week 4 was 55.

The student's math score went up 30 points from Week 6 to Week 12.

The score went up possibly because the student studied harder or found a helpful tutor.

The score dropped in Week 17, possibly because the student didn't study that week.

It makes sense not to connect the points because scores are discrete values, they do not continually change by the second.

Determining Whether a Relation Is a Function

A relation is any set of ordered pairs or the mapping between a set of inputs and a set of outputs. The first coordinate of an ordered pair in a relation is the input, and the second coordinate is the output. A function maps each input to one and only one output. Relations that are not functions will have more than one output for each input.

Example

Input	Output
−10	20
−5	10
0	0
5	10
10	20

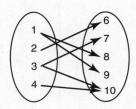

The ordered pairs are (−10, 20), (−5, 10), (0, 0), (5, 10), and (10, 20). Even though there are outputs, or *y*-values, with more than one input, there are no inputs, or *x*-values, with more than one output. So, this relation is a function.

The ordered pairs are (1, 8), (1, 9), (2, 6), (3, 7), (3, 10), and (4, 10). There is more than one output for the inputs 1 and 3. So, this relation is not a function.

2.3 Determining Whether a Graph or Scatter Plot Is a Function

A scatter plot is a graph of a collection of ordered pairs that allows an exploration of the relationship between the points. The vertical line test is a visual method of determining whether a relation represented on a coordinate plane is a function. To apply the vertical line test, consider all of the vertical lines that could be drawn on the graph of a relation. If any of the vertical lines intersects the graph of the relation at more than one point, then the relation is not a function.

Example

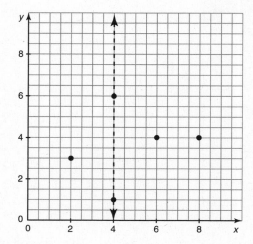

The vertical line test intersects the graph at two points, (4, 1) and (4, 6). So, the relation is not a function.

2.3 Determining Whether an Equation Is a Function

To test if an equation is a function, first substitute values for x into the equation, and then determine if any x-value can be mapped to more than one y-value. If each x-value has exactly one y-value, then it is a function. Otherwise, it is not a function.

Example

$y = 5x + 12$ is a function because no x-value can be mapped to more than one y-value. Some examples of ordered pairs are (0, 12), (1, 17), (2, 22), and (3, 27).

2.3 Determining Whether a Context Describes a Function

If each input in a context has exactly one output, then it is a function. Otherwise it is not a function.

Example

Input: A garden nursery sends a catalog to each customer on its preferred customer list. *Output*: Each preferred customer gets one catalog.

The relation is a function because each customer gets one catalog.

2

2.4 Graphing Linear Functions

When graphing the input and output values of some functions, the graph forms a straight line. Such functions are called linear functions.

Example

Tristan is filling his swimming pool with water. The water depth increases by 4 inches every hour. The input-output table displays the water depth in the pool for the first 8 hours.

Time (hours)	Water Depth (inches)
0	0
1	4
2	8
3	12
4	16
5	20
6	24
7	28
8	32

The equation $d = 4t$ can be used to model the water depth, d, after t hours.

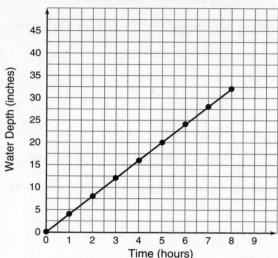

Water Depth in Tristan's Pool

The graph displays the water depth for the first 8 hours. The variable, d, is the dependent variable, because the depth of the water in the pool depends on the amount of time which has passed. The variable, t, is the independent variable.

2.5 Using Tables, Graphs, and Equations

Tables, graphs, and equations can provide different representations of the same problem situation. In a problem, when one variable depends on another variable it is called the dependent variable. The other variable is called the independent variable because it does not depend on the dependent variable.

Example

Chanise wants to record some CDs of her music. CD Cutz studio charges a start-up fee of $50 and then $3 for every CD produced.

The cost of producing 30 CDs is $30(3) + 50 = 90 + 50 = \$140$.
The cost of producing 40 CDs is $40(3) + 50 = 120 + 50 = \$170$.
The cost of producing 50 CDs is $50(3) + 50 = 150 + 50 = \$200$.

If Chanise has $250 to spend on CDs, the number of CDs she can produce can be determined by working backwards.

$$\text{Number of CDs: } \frac{250 - 50}{3} = \frac{200}{3} \approx 66.67$$

Chanise can produce 66 CDs with $250.

The table of values shown represents the problem situation.

Number of CDs Produced	Total Cost (dollars)
30	140
40	170
50	200
60	230
80	290
100	350

Letters can represent the variables in the problem and determine which variable is the independent variable and which is the dependent variable.

The variable x represents the number of CDs produced. The variable C represents the total cost to produce the CDs in dollars. The variable C is the dependent variable because its value depends on the number of CDs produced, x. The variable x is the independent variable.

A graph can be created based on the data in your table.

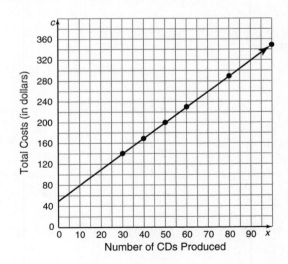

The equation $C = 3x + 50$ represents the problem situation. In the equation, C represents the total cost, in dollars, of producing x CDs.

2.6 Estimating Values of Expressions that Involve Decimals

When an exact value of an expression is not needed, estimation can be used to determine an approximate value. One way to estimate is to use rounding.

Example

The estimated value of the expression is shown.

$$83.90 - 48.05 + 14.22$$
$$84 - 48 + 14 = 50$$
$$83.90 - 48.05 + 14.22 \approx 50$$

2.6 Using the Point of Intersection to Compare Two Models

In a graph of two lines, the point of intersection is the point at which the two lines cross. When graphing two cost models, the point of intersection is the point at which the two costs are equal.

Example

Chanise is trying to decide where to produce her newest music CD. The cost, in dollars, of producing CDs at CD Cutz is represented by the equation $C = 3x + 50$. The cost, in dollars, of producing CDs at The CD Barn is represented by the equation $C = 2x + 100$. In each equation, C represents the total cost of producing x CDs. The graph shows the total cost of producing CDs at each studio.

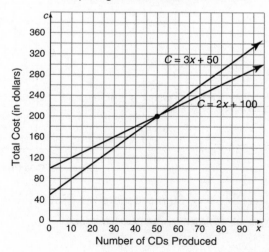

According to the graph, the cost of producing CDs at each studio is the same when Chanise produces 50 CDs. Each studio would charge $200 to produce 50 CDs. CD Cutz costs less than The CD Barn when Chanise produces fewer than 50 CDs. The CD Barn costs less than CD Cutz when Chanise produces more than 50 CDs.

2.7 Graphing Non-Linear Functions

There are many different types of non-linear functions. Several common non-linear functions are absolute value functions, square or quadratic functions, and cube or cubic functions. Each of these types of functions has a very distinctive shape.

Examples

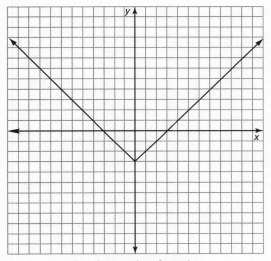

absolute value function

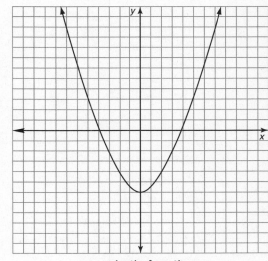

quadratic function

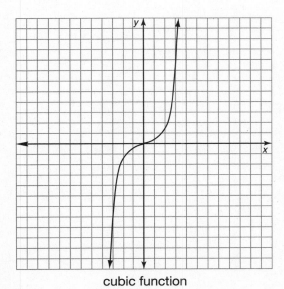

cubic function

3 ANALYZING LINEAR EQUATIONS

Skiers seek soft, freshly fallen snow because it gives a smooth, "floating" ride down the mountain. Ski tracks in the snow also provide a record of each skier's path.

3.1

HITTING THE SLOPES
Determining Rate of Change from a Graph

3

Learning Goals

In this lesson, you will:

▶ Determine the rate of change from a graph.

▶ Create a scenario, a table, and an equation from a graph.

▶ Connect the rate of change represented in a graph to the rate of change in other representations.

▶ Use $\frac{rise}{run}$ to calculate the rate of change from a graph.

▶ Determine if a graph has a rate of change that is increasing, decreasing, zero, or undefined.

▶ Compare unit rates of change in the same graph.

Key Terms

▶ rate

▶ rate of change

▶ per

▶ unit rate

▶ rise

▶ run

▶ $\frac{rise}{run}$

You may have seen road grade signs before. These signs often show a car going down a road at an angle. Below this picture is a percent. What does this percent mean?

Well, if you see a sign that reads "8%," that means that the road you are on is going down (or up) 8 feet for every 100 feet you drive.

8 ft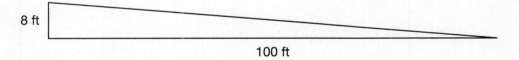

100 ft

How much would you go up or down if the road stayed at 8% for one mile?

Problem 1   Hit the Slopes

The linear graph shown is a model of a skier's elevation, over time, while skiing down a hill.

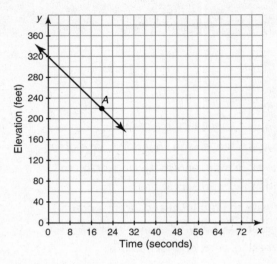

1. What does point A on the graph represent?

2. At what elevation did the skier start? Label the point on the graph representing your answer with the letter B.

3. Why do you think the graph extends beyond the y-axis?

4. About how many seconds would it take for the skier to reach the bottom of the hill? Explain your reasoning.

5. How many feet did the skier descend down the hill each second? Explain your reasoning.

6. Label (24, 200) with C. How could you use points A and C to calculate the number of feet the skier descended each second?

A **rate** is a ratio in which the two quantities being compared are measured in different units. Rates are commonly written in fractional form, with the dependent variable as the numerator, and the independent variable as the denominator.

A **rate of change** is used to describe the rate of increase or decrease.

For this problem, you can write a rate to compare the change in elevation to the change in time:

A ratio is a comparison of two quantities that are measured in the same units.

$$\frac{\text{change in elevation}}{\text{change in time}} \quad \begin{array}{l} \longleftarrow \quad \text{dependent variable} \\ \longleftarrow \quad \text{independent variable} \end{array}$$

This rate is read as "change in elevation *per* change in time." **Per** means "for each" or "for every."

7. Write a rate to compare the change in elevation to the change in time at point A. Describe what the rate means. Make sure to state whether the rate is a rate of increase or a rate of decrease.

8. Write a rate to compare the change in elevation to the change in time at point *C*. Describe what the rate means. Make sure to state whether the rate is a rate of increase or a rate of decrease.

A **unit rate** is a comparison of two measurements in which the denominator has a value of one unit.

9. Write the rates of change at points *A* and *C* as unit rates.

10. What do you notice about these unit rates? Explain your observation.

11. What are the independent and dependent variables in the graph?

Remember, the domain is the set of all inputs and the range is the set of all outputs.

12. What is the domain of the problem situation? Include units in your response.

13. What is the range of the problem situation? Include units in your response.

14. What is the unit rate of change modeled in the graph? Use numerical values and units. State whether it is a rate of increase or a rate of decrease.

15. Write in sentence form what is happening in the problem. Include:

- the initial values of the independent and dependent variables in the context of the problem;

- a sentence explaining the rate of change in terms of the context of the problem; and

- the final values of the independent and dependent variables in the context of the problem.

You can calculate the rate of change from a graph.

Complete these steps to determine the rate of change shown in the graph.

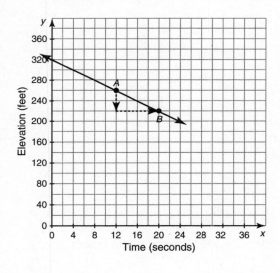 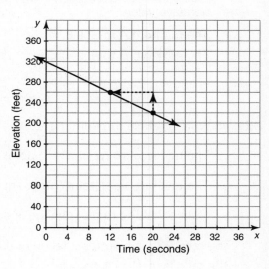

Step 1: Choose two points on the line. Choose points with coordinate values that can be read without estimation. The two points shown are Points *A* and *B*.

Step 2: Determine the *rise*. The **rise** is the vertical change from the first point to the second point.

Use the scale when counting. If you are determining the rise from point A to point B, the rise will be a negative value. If you are determining the rise from point B to point A, the rise will have a positive value.

The rise from A to B is -40.

The rise from B to A is 40.

Step 3: Continue from the point where you left off on the graph to complete the next step. Determine the *run*. The **run** is the horizontal change from the first point to the second point.

Use the scale when counting. If you are determining the run from point A to point B, then the run will have a positive value.

If you are determining the run from point B to point A, then the run will have a negative value.

The run from A to B is 8.

The run from B to A is -8.

Step 4: Write a rate in the format $\frac{rise}{run}$.

The unit rate from point A to point B is $\frac{-40}{8} = \frac{-5}{1}$.

The unit rate from point B to point A is $\frac{40}{-8} = \frac{5}{-1}$.

Notice that the rate of change is equal no matter which point you start from.

The ratio $\frac{\textbf{rise}}{\textbf{run}}$ is a representation of the rate of change shown in the graph.

The ratio is read as "rise over run."

16. Why is the rise the value for the numerator and the run the value for the denominator?

17. What does it mean if a rate of change is negative?

Problem 2   Rise and Then Run

The ratio $\frac{\text{rise}}{\text{run}}$ was used either correctly or incorrectly to determine the rate of change in the following graphs shown. Each graph models the same problem.

- Follow the arrows to write the rate of change.
- Explain any errors in the process of drawing the arrows.

1.

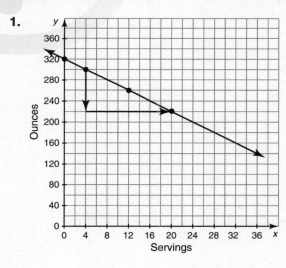

2.

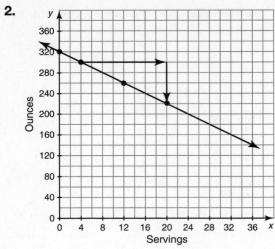

3.

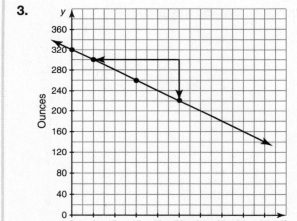

Problem 3   Selecting Coordinate Points

1. Shelley read the rate of change from the graph shown as $\dfrac{1 \text{ dollar}}{2 \text{ tickets}}$, or $1 for every 2 tickets. She plotted points on the graph to show the values she used to determine the rate of change.

The line drawn models the relationship. Do all the points on the line make sense in this problem situation

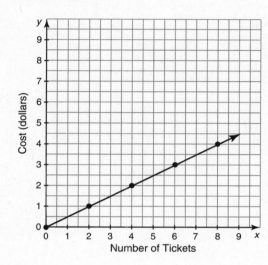

a. Restate the rate of change as a unit rate. Explain its meaning. Show your work.

b. Why do you think Shelley did not read the unit rate of change from the graph?

2. Determine the rate of change from the graph shown. Plot points on the graph to show the values you used to determine the rate.

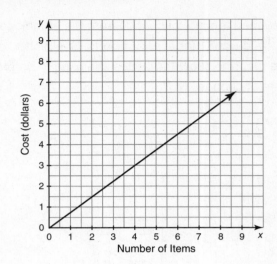

Choose points that can be read without estimation.

3. Restate the rate of change as a unit rate. Explain its meaning.

4. What is the cost of 10 items? Show your work.

5. Do you prefer to use the original rate of change determined from the graph, or the unit rate when making calculations? Explain your reasoning.

6. Calculate the rate of change from the graph shown. Plot points on the graph to show the values you used to determine the rate.

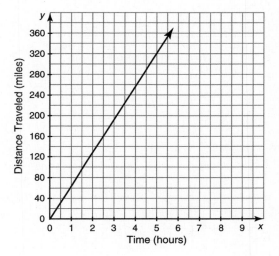

7. Restate the rate as a unit rate. Explain its meaning.

1. Determine the rate of change from each graph.

a.

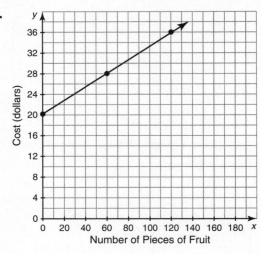

b.

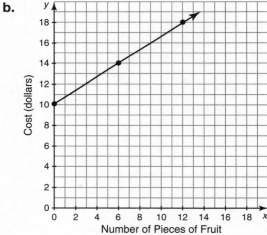

c. The two graphs look exactly alike. How could they show different rates of change?

2. Determine the rate of change from each graph.

a.

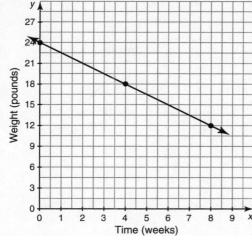

b.

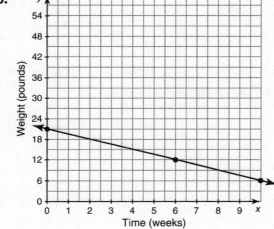

c. The two graphs look different. How could they show the same rate of change?

3. Determine the unit rate of change for each graph.

a.

b.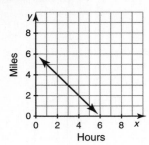

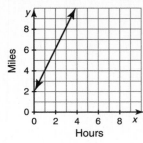

Any ratio with a denominator of 0 is undefined.

$$\frac{any\ value}{0} = undefined$$

c.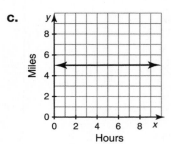

d.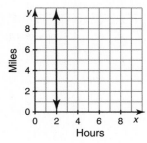

e. How can you tell from the graph whether the rate of change will be positive or negative before determining $\frac{rise}{run}$?

f. Describe the graph's direction if the rate of change is equal to zero.

g. Describe the graph's direction if the rate of change is undefined.

Talk the Talk

The graph shown represents the distance four cars travel over time.

1. Calculate the unit rate for each car. Show your work.

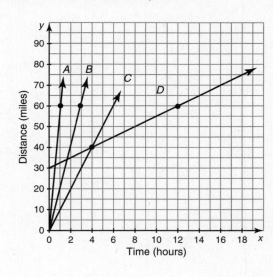

2. Describe how the steepness of the line is related to the rate of change.

Be prepared to share your solutions and methods.

3.2

AT THE ARCADE
Determining Rate of Change from a Table

Learning Goals

In this lesson, you will:

▶ Determine the rate of change from a table of values.

▶ Create a graph, a context, and an equation from a table of values.

▶ Connect the rate of change represented in a table of values to the rate of change in other representations.

▶ Use $\frac{y_2 - y_1}{x_2 - x_1}$ to calculate the rate of change from a table of values or two coordinate pairs.

▶ Determine whether a table of values will make a straight line if graphed.

Key Term

▶ first differences

3

Some call them crane games or teddy pickers or grab machines or claw games. These machines can be found inside restaurants, arcades, supermarkets, and even movie theaters. Although there are many different kinds, these games usually involve controlling a claw to pick up a prize, like a stuffed toy, a doll, or candy.

Have you ever won a prize from one of these games?

Problem 1   At the Arcade

Ron has a player's card for the arcade at the mall. His player's card keeps track of the number of credits he earns as he wins games. Each winning game earns the same number of credits, and those credits can be redeemed for various prizes. Ron has been saving his credits to collect a prize worth 500 credits.

The table shows the number of credits Ron had on his game card at various times today when he checked his balance at the arcade.

Number of Games Ron Won Today	Number of Credits on Ron's Player's Card
0	120
12	216
18	264
25	320
40	440

1. Explain the meaning of the ordered pair (0, 120) listed in the table.

2. Write a rate to compare the change in credits earned to the change in games won. Show your work.

3. Write the rate as a unit rate and explain its meaning.

4. Recalculate the unit rate by using different values from the table. Show your work.

5. Analyze Rhonda's calculations shown.

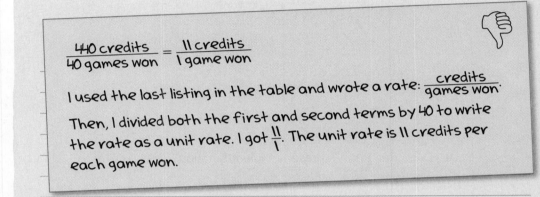

$$\frac{440\ credits}{40\ games\ won} = \frac{11\ credits}{1\ game\ won}$$

I used the last listing in the table and wrote a rate: $\frac{credits}{games\ won}$.

Then, I divided both the first and second terms by 40 to write the rate as a unit rate. I got $\frac{11}{1}$. The unit rate is 11 credits per each game won.

Explain to Rhonda why her calculations are incorrect.

6. Before Ron started winning games today, how many games had he won for which he had saved the credits on his player's card? Show your work.

7. After Ron won his fortieth game today, how many more games does he need to win to collect a prize worth 500 credits? Show your work and explain your reasoning.

8. Create a graph to represent the information from the previous table. Include scales and labels.

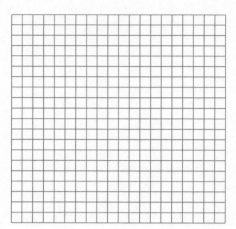

How does your graph represent the independent and dependent values?

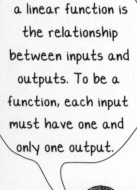

Remember, a linear function is the relationship between inputs and outputs. To be a function, each input must have one and only one output.

a. Does the graph represent a linear function? Explain why or why not.

b. Calculate the rate of change from the graph. Show your work.

9. What is the domain of the problem situation? Include units in your response.

10. What is the range of the problem situation? Include units in your response.

11. What is the unit rate of change modeled in the graph? Use numerical values and units. State whether it is a rate of increase or a rate of decrease.

12. Write in sentence form what is happening in the problem. Include:

- the initial values of the independent and dependent variables in the context of the problem;
- a sentence explaining the rate of change in terms of the context of the problem; and
- the final values of the independent and dependent variables in the context of the problem.

Problem 2 Calculating Rate of Change from a Table

So far, you have determined the rate of change from a graph using the $\frac{rise}{run}$ method. However, you can also determine the rate of change from a table.

1. Complete the steps to determine the rate of change from a table.

Number of Games Ron Won Today	Number of Credits on Ron's Player's Card
0	120
12	216
18	264
25	320
40	440

Step 1: Choose any two values of the independent variable. Calculate their difference.

Step 2: Calculate the difference between the corresponding values of the dependent variable. It is important that the order of values you used for determining the difference of the independent variables be followed for the dependent variables.

Step 3: Write a rate to compare the change in the dependent variable to the change in the independent variable.

Step 4: Rewrite the rate as a unit rate.

2. This method was used either correctly or incorrectly to determine the rate of change in the three tables shown, each one modeling the same problem.

- Follow the arrows to calculate the rate of change. Show your work.

- Explain any errors that may have occurred when the arrows were drawn.

Example 1

Number of Games Ron Won Today	Number of Credits on Ron's Player's Card
Games	Credits
0	120
12	216
18	264
25	320
40	440

Example 2

Number of Games Ron Won Today	Number of Credits on Ron's Player's Card
Games	Credits
0	120
12	216
18	264
25	320
40	440

Example 3

Number of Games Ron Won Today	Number of Credits on Ron's Player's Card
Games	Credits
0	120
12	216
18	264
25	320
40	440

This method of determining a rate of change is not a formal method. It can be referred to as an informal method for determining a rate of change.

There is a formal mathematical process that can be used to calculate the rate of change of a linear function from a table of values with at least two coordinate pairs.

The rate of change of the linear function can be calculated using two ordered pairs and the formula:

$$\text{rate of change of a linear function} = \frac{y_2 - y_1}{x_2 - x_1},$$

where the first point is at (x_1, y_1) and the second point is at (x_2, y_2).

For example, let's consider the table that shows the number of credits Ron had on his game card at various times when he checked his balance at the arcade.

Number of Games Ron Won Today	Number of Credits on Ron's Player's Card
0	120
12	216
18	264
25	320
40	440

Step 1: From the table of values, use (12, 216) as the first point and (25, 320) as the second point.

Step 2: Label the points with the variables.

(12, 216) (25, 320)
↓   ↓   ↓   ↓
(x_1, y_1) (x_2, y_2)

Step 3: Use the formula for the rate of change of a linear function and substitution.

By substitution: $\dfrac{y_2 - y_1}{x_2 - x_1} = \dfrac{320 - 216}{25 - 12}$

$$= \frac{104}{13}$$

$$= \frac{8}{1}$$

The rate of change is $\dfrac{8 \text{ credits}}{1 \text{ game}}$.

3. Repeat the process to calculate the rate of change using two different values from the table. Show all work.

Which points will you choose? Does it make a difference?

4. How is using the formula for a table related to using $\frac{\text{rise}}{\text{run}}$ for a graph?

3

5. Calculate the unit rate of change of each linear function using the formula. Show all work.

a.

Number of Carnival Ride Tickets	Cost (dollars)
4	9
8	12
16	18
32	30

Analyze the values in the table before you start calculating the rate of change...do you think the rate of change will be positive or negative?

b.

x	y
−1	13
0	−2
4	−62
10	−152

c.

Days Passed	Vitamins Remaining in Bottle
7	25
8	23
9	21
10	19

d.

x	y
7	9
18	9
29	9
40	9

6. Only two points are necessary to use the informal method or the formula to calculate the rate of change of a linear function. Given two points:

- use the informal method to determine the rate of change; and
- use the formula to determine the rate of change.

a. (10, 25) and (55, 40)

x	y
10	25
55	40

b. (4, 19) and (16, 5)

x	y
4	19
24	3

c. Which method do you prefer, the informal one or the formula? Explain your choice.

Problem 3　Is that Relation Linear?

If the rate of change between every pair of ordered pairs in a table of values is the same, or constant, then the ordered pairs, when plotted, will form a straight line.

To determine if a table represents a linear function, you can calculate the rate of change between every consecutive pair of ordered pairs and make sure you obtain the same value every time.

1. Calculate the rate of change between the points represented by the given ordered pairs. Show your work.

x	y
4	13
9	28
11	34
16	47

a. (4, 13) and (9, 28)

b. (9, 28) and (11, 34)

> You can think about the rate of change as the difference between the y-values over the difference between the x-values.

c. (11, 34) and (16, 47)

d. Will the ordered pairs listed in the table form a straight line when plotted? Explain your reasoning.

2. Determine whether the ordered pairs listed in each table will form a straight line when plotted. Show your work. Explain your reasoning.

a.

x	y
2	7
6	13
8	16
20	34

b.

x	y
1	33
2	40
3	47
4	54
5	61

3. What was different about the table in Question 2, part (b)? How did that affect your calculations?

When the values for the independent variable in a table are consecutive integers, you can examine only the column with the dependent variable and calculate the differences between consecutive values. If the differences are the same each time, then you know that the rate of change is the same each time. The ordered pairs in the table will therefore form a straight line when plotted.

> Consecutive means one right after the other like 12, 13, and 14.

The differences have been calculated for the table shown.

x	y	
1	99	
2	86	$99 - 86 = -13$
3	73	$86 - 73 = -13$
4	60	$60 - 47 = -13$
5	47	

The differences between consecutive values for the dependent variable are the same each time. So, the rate of change is the same each time as well. The ordered pairs in this table will therefore form a straight line when plotted.

> So, each time you add 1 to the x-value the y-value decreases by the same value.

In this process, you are calculating *first differences*. **First differences** are the values determined by subtracting consecutive *y*-values in a table when the *x*-values are consecutive integers.

4. Determine whether the ordered pairs in each table will form straight lines when plotted. Show your work and explain your reasoning.

a.

x	y
1	25
2	34
3	45
4	52
5	61

b.

x	y
1	12
2	8
3	4
4	0
5	−4

c.

x	y
1	1
2	4
3	9
4	16
5	25

d.

x	y
1	15
2	18
3	21
4	24
5	27

Looking at the first differences identifies whether or not there is a constant rate of change in the table values.

Be prepared to share your solutions and methods.

TO PUT IT IN CONTEXT
Determining Rate of Change from a Context

Learning Goals

In this lesson, you will:

▶ Determine the rate of change from a context.

▶ Create a graph, a table, and an equation from a context.

▶ Connect the rate of change represented in a context to the rate of change in other representations.

▶ Generate the values of two coordinate pairs from information given in context.

Context is important. The word usually refers to all the events or thoughts surrounding what someone says or writes. When someone takes another person's words "out of context," he or she is usually quoting what the other person said without considering all the events surrounding what that person said.

Can you give some other examples of context? What other ways can people take another person's words or deeds "out of context"?

Problem 1   Soccer Tournament

The Salem Middle School soccer team travels to a tournament. They began their bus trip the evening before the tournament by traveling 210 miles and staying overnight at a hotel. The following morning, they continued their trip by traveling an additional three hours until they reached their destination 180 miles from the hotel. They arrived there in time for their tournament, which began at 11:00 AM.

1. What is the rate at which the bus traveled during the second portion of the trip? Show your work.

2. What was the total distance of the trip? Show your work.

3. If the bus traveled the same average rate during both segments of the trip, what is the total number of hours the team traveled on the bus? Show your work.

4. Why do you think the team did not make the entire trip the morning of the tournament?

5. Complete the graph to represent the context.

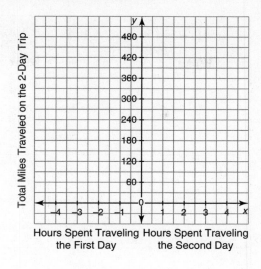

6. Explain why the graph represents a linear function.

7. Demonstrate the rate of change graphically and by using the formula.
Show your work.

8. What is happening in terms of the context in the second quadrant of the graph?

9. Complete the table representing the context.

Travel Time for Second Day (hours)	Total Miles Traveled on the Two-Day Trip

10. The unit rate (miles per hour) is **not** an entry in the table. Calculate the unit rate using the table of values. Show your work.

11. Recalculate the unit rate by using different values from the table. Show your work.

The unit rate will be "change in y" over "change of 1 in x."

Problem 2   Calculating Rate of Change from a Context

Write the rate described in each context.

1. Bella's Pizza Shop charges $4.50 for a small pizza, $7 for a medium pizza, and $9 for a large pizza. Toppings cost extra depending on the size of the pizza ordered. Bruce ordered a large pizza with three toppings that cost a total of $12.60. What is the unit rate of cost per number of toppings for a large pizza? Show your work.

> Do you remember what you must do when determining an answer that is comparing different units of measure?

2. A maintenance crew is paving a road. They are able to pave one-eighth of a mile of road during each working shift. A working shift is 7 hours. What is the unit rate of yards of road paved per hour? Show your work.

3. Melanie baked breakfast rolls for a band camp fundraiser. She baked 15 dozen breakfast rolls in 3 hours.

   a. What is the average rate of breakfast rolls baked per minute?

   b. Why do you think that "average" rate is asked instead of "rate"?

Remember, before you can calculate a profit, you must first deduct the expenses that must be paid first.

4. One hundred twenty teenagers attended the community center's dance. Each ticket costs $5. The community center's expenses for the dance are $140 for the disc jockey (DJ), and $60 for other expenses. What is the profit the center made in dollars for each ticket sold?
Show your work.

5. Jonathan goes to bed at 9:30 PM on school nights and wakes up at 6:00 AM. On Fridays and Saturdays, he goes to bed at 11:00 PM and wakes up at 9:00 AM. What is Jonathan's average rate of sleep hours per night? Show your work.

6. Mike had a balance of $81 on his credit card for a department store. He just purchased 3 sweatshirts, and his balance is now $146.85. What is the cost of one sweatshirt? Show your work.

7. One dieter in a weight-loss contest weighed 149 pounds after 8 weeks on his diet. By Week 13, he weighed 134 pounds. What was his average weight loss per week? Show your work.

8. Kathy is working after school to finish assembling the 82 favors needed for the school dance. When she starts at 3:15 PM, she counts the 67 favors that are already assembled. She works until 4:30 PM to finish the job.

   a. How many favors can Kathy assemble in a minute?

   b. How many minutes does it take Kathy to assemble one favor?

   c. Which rate is more meaningful in this situation? Explain your reasoning.

9. Eddie rented a moving van to travel across the country. The odometer registered 34,567 miles after he drove for 4 hours. After 7 hours of driving, the odometer read 34,741 miles.

   a. What was Eddie's driving rate in miles per hour?

b. When Eddie calculated his driving rate, he converted the information to coordinate points and then used the formula $\frac{y_2 - y_1}{x_2 - x_1}$. Examine his work.

The points are (4, 34,567) and (7, 34,741).
Using the formula $\frac{y_2 - y_1}{x_2 - x_1}$, I got $\frac{34,741 - 34,567}{7 - 4} = \frac{174}{3} = \frac{58}{1}$.
This means that on average I was traveling 58 miles per hour.

How does your process of calculating Eddie's driving rate compare to his work?

10. Julie used her gift card for the local coffee shop to buy iced teas for herself and five friends. After she and one friend placed their orders, the balance on Julie's gift card was $14.85. After all 6 members of the group got their iced teas, she had a balance of $3.97 on her gift card.

Use Eddie's method from Question 9, part (b) to determine the cost for one glass of iced tea. Show all work.

Be prepared to share your solutions and methods.

ALL TOGETHER NOW!

3.4

Determining Rate of Change from an Equation

3

The Duquesne (pronounced "doo - KANE") Incline in Pittsburgh, Pennsylvania is what is known as a funicular (foo - NICK - you - lur). A funicular is a railway that pulls cars up and down a slope. Funiculars played important roles in many cities' histories. Funiculars were ways people could commute to work from their homes in hillsides to factories along river banks.

The Duquesne Incline, which has a slope of 30°, is one of the most popular tourist attractions in Pittsburgh.

Problem 1 Cut and Sort Linear Relations

1. Carefully cut out the graphs, tables, contexts, and equations on the following pages. Match each equation with its correct graph, table, or context. Explain how you matched the equations with the representations.

It's time to cut and sort! Better take out your scissors.

2. Compare the graphs.

   a. How are they different? How can you tell this difference by looking at their equations?

   b. Analyze the point where each graph crosses the y-axis. How can you tell this point by looking at the equation for each graph?

   c. What is the rate of change for each graph? How is the rate of change represented in each equation?

3. Analyze the equation for each table.

   a. Determine the coefficient of x for each equation using a formula.

Can you remember the ways to determine the rate of change from a table?

   b. How can the number that is added in each equation be determined from the table?

4. Analyze the equation for each context. Explain what each term of the equation means in each context.

3

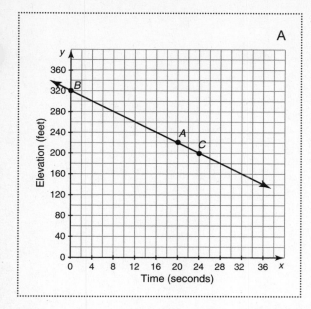

A

B

Michele read the first 40 pages of a mystery novel before she fell asleep. The next day, she read one page every two minutes until she finished the book, which was a total of 325 pages.

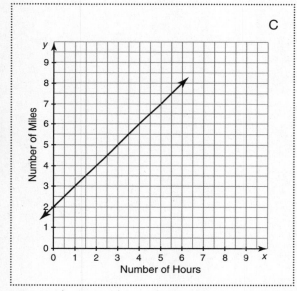

C

D

Number of Carnival Ride Tickets	Cost (in dollars)
x	y
0	6
4	9
8	12
16	18
32	30

F

Bella's Pizza Shop charges $4.50 for a small pizza, $7.00 for a medium pizza, and $9.00 for a large pizza. Additional toppings cost extra depending on the size of the pizza ordered. Bruce ordered a large pizza with three toppings that cost a total of $12.60.

E

Number of Games Ron Won Today	Number of Credits on Ron's Player's Card
x	y
0	120
12	216
18	264
25	320
40	440

$y = 1.2x + 9$	$y = \dfrac{3}{4}x + 6$
$y = \dfrac{1}{2}x + 40$	$y = x + 2$
$y = -5x + 320$	$y = 8x + 120$

So far, you have determined the rate of change either through formal and informal methods. Now you will learn about a new name for a rate of change. **Slope** is another mathematical term for rate of change. The slope of a line can be calculated in the same ways as rate of change is calculated:

• from a graph using $\frac{\text{rise}}{\text{run}}$ as a measure of the steepness of a line;

• from a table using $\frac{y_2 - y_1}{x_2 - x_1}$ or informally through subtraction of table values;

• from an equation that has been solved for y, as the coefficient of x; and

• from a context using text clues or coordinate point values given in the problem.

All of these methods are also leading us to explore the *slope-intercept form*. The **slope-intercept form** of a linear equation is $y = mx + b$, where m is the slope of the line.

So, to see the slope of a line from an equation, you should first solve the equation for y.

Problem 2 Calculating Rate of Change from an Equation

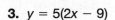

If a linear equation is solved for y, the coefficient of x represents the rate of change, or slope of the line. Determine the slopes of the lines represented by each equation. Show your work.

1. $y = 3x - 9 + 8x$

2. $15x + 3y = 300$

3. $y = 5(2x - 9)$

4. $8y = -6x + 24$

5. $y = x - 3$

6. $y = 9$

7. $4x - 12y = 48$

8. $x = 10$

Problem 3 Investigating Rate of Change from an Equation

You can also use a graphing calculator to investigate slopes. First you will explore the slope for the equation $y = 1x$.

Step 1: Press $\boxed{Y =}$. Your cursor should be blinking next to $Y_1 =$. Enter **1x**. Then, press $\boxed{\textbf{GRAPH}}$.

You will refer to this basic graph as you make changes to the coefficient of x.

Step 2: Press $\boxed{Y =}$. Using the arrow keys, move to the left to the \ in front of Y_1.

Step 3: Press $\boxed{\textbf{ENTER}}$ one time until the \ is darkened. Press $\boxed{\textbf{GRAPH}}$. Your basic graph should be darkened for easy reference.

1. Press $\boxed{Y =}$.
Next to Y_2, enter **4x**.

a. What do you think this graph will look like in comparison to the graph of $y = 1x$? Verify your answer by pressing $\boxed{\textbf{GRAPH}}$.

b. Write an equation of another line that is steeper than both of these lines. Verify your answer by entering the equation next to **Y₃** and graphing it.

c. How does increasing the coefficient of x affect the rate of change and the graph of the line?

2. Keep the equation $y_1 = 1x$ on the calculator. Clear all other equations.

a. Write an equation of a line that is less steep than $y_1 = 1x$. Verify your answer by entering the equation next to **Y₂** and graphing it.

To clear all the other equations, highlight the Y=line and press CLEAR.

b. Write an equation of a line that is less steep than both of these lines. Verify your answer by entering the equation next to **Y₃** and graphing it.

c. How does decreasing the coefficient of x affect the rate of change and the graph of the line?

3. Keep the equation $y_1 = 1x$ on the calculator. Clear all other equations.

Press $\boxed{\mathbf{Y} =}$.

Next to $\mathbf{Y_2}$, enter $-\mathbf{1x}$. Use the $(-)$ sign.

Remember to use the negative button–not the subtraction button!

a. What do you think this graph will look like in comparison to the graph of $y = 1x$? Verify your answer by pressing $\boxed{\mathbf{GRAPH}}$.

b. Write an equation of another line that is slanted in the same direction as $y = -1x$ but is steeper than that line. Verify your answer by entering the equation next to $\mathbf{Y_3}$ and graphing it.

c. Write an equation of another line that is slanted in the same direction as $y = -1x$ but is less steep than that line. Verify your answer by entering the equation next to $\mathbf{Y_4}$ and graphing it.

d. How does a negative coefficient of x affect the rate of change and the graph of the line?

4. Clear all equations including $y_1 = 1x$ from the calculator.

a. Enter the equation $y = 1$.

What do you think this graph will look like? Verify your answer by pressing GRAPH .

b. What is the coefficient of x?

c. How does a coefficient of 0 affect the rate of change and the graph of the line?

d. Why do you think it is impossible to graph the equation $x = 1$ on the graphing calculator?

So, in the equation $y = mx + b$, the m represents the slope. What does the b represent? Anything?

Be prepared to share your solutions and methods.

3.5

WHERE IT CROSSES

Determining y-Intercepts from Various Representations

Learning Goals

In this lesson, you will:

▶ Determine the *y*-intercept of a linear function from a context, a table, a graph, or an equation.

▶ Write the *y*-intercept in coordinate form.

▶ Explain the meaning of the *y*-intercept when given the context of a linear function.

▶ Explain how the *y*-intercept is useful in graphing a linear function.

▶ Explain what makes a relationship a direct variation.

Key Terms

▶ *y*-intercept

▶ direct variation

I n professional football, an interception occurs when the ball is thrown by a player on one team and is caught by a player on the opposing team.

As of 2011, the person with the most career interceptions was a man born in Flint, Michigan, in 1942 and played for the Washington Redskins and the Minnesota Vikings.

Can you name him? How many interceptions did he catch?

Problem 1   Connecting Representations

Questions 1 through 5 provide guidance for completing the graphic organizer that follows.

1. Read the context. Represent that information in the form of a graph, a table, and an equation.

2. Revisit each representation. In each box, show how the rate of change is represented.

The rate of change is one important feature of a linear function. Another important feature is the *y-intercept*. The **y-intercept** is the *y*-coordinate of the point where a graph crosses the *y*-axis. The *y*-intercept can also be written in the form (0, *y*).

3. Mark the *y*-intercept on the graph. Label the *y*-intercept in coordinate form.

4. What is the meaning of the *y*-intercept in the context?

5. Revisit each representation. Mark where the *y*-intercept is evident in the context, the table, and the equation.

Eva keeps track of the hours she devotes to volunteering. When she began volunteering on a regular basis at Children's Hospital, she already had 60 volunteer hours at other events. After three weeks of working at Children's Hospital, she had another 36 hours of volunteering.

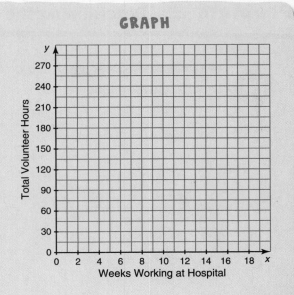

3

MULTIPLE REPRESENTATIONS

Number of Weeks Volunteering at the Hospital	Total Hours Volunteering

Let **y** represent:

Let **x** represent:

Problem 2   Determining the y-Intercept from a Graph

Examine each linear graph and determine the y-intercept. Write the y-intercept in coordinate form. Show all work.

1.

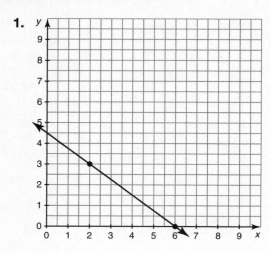

2.

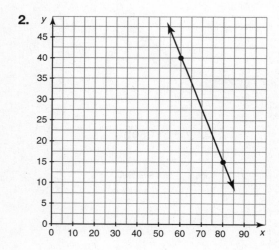

How can you use the rate of change shown to think about where each graph would cross the y-axis?

3.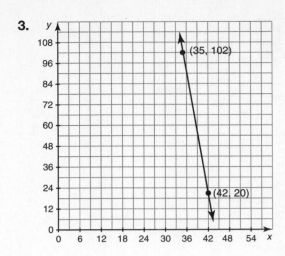

Problem 3   Determining the y-Intercept from a Table

Each table represents a linear function. Use the table to identify the y-intercept. Write the y-intercept in coordinate form. Show all work.

1.

x	y
200	14
225	16
250	18
275	20
300	22

So, if the y-intercept was given in any table would the x-value be 0 or the y-value be 0?

2.

x	y
100	10
105	6
110	2
115	−2
120	−6

3.

x	y
16	90
19	91
22	92
25	93
28	94

How does knowing the rate of change help you determine the y-intercept?

Problem 4 Determining the *y*-Intercept from a Context

Each context represents a linear function. Read each and determine the *y*-intercept. Write the *y*-intercept in coordinate form. Show all work. Explain what the *y*-intercept represents in the problem situation.

1. Kim spent $18 to purchase a ride-all-day pass for the amusement park and to play 8 games. After playing a total of 20 games, she realized she'd spent $24.

2. Mitch saved money he received as gifts to buy a bike. When he added one week's allowance to his savings, he had $125. After 3 more weeks of saving his allowance, he had $161 toward the cost of his bike.

3. The cost to ship a package in the mail includes a basic shipping charge plus an additional cost per number of pounds the package weighs. A three-pound package costs $6.30 to ship. A ten-pound package costs $14 to ship.

Problem 5   Determining the *y*-Intercept from an Equation

Each equation represents a linear function. Examine each and determine the *y*-intercept. Write the *y*-intercept in coordinate form. Show all work.

1. $4x + 6y = 270$

2. $8x - 4y = 225$

When *x* is 0, that's where the graph crosses the *y*-axis.

3. $y + 9 = 6(x - 3)$

Problem 6   A Special Case of a Linear Equation

Questions 1 through 3 provide guidance for completing the graphic organizer that follows.

1. Read the context. Represent that information in the form of a graph, a table, and an equation.

2. In each box, show how the rate of change is represented.

3. In each box, show how the *y*-intercept is represented.

4. What is the *y*-intercept? Explain what the *y*-intercept represents in the problem.

CONTEXT

The basketball team won the championship. They are selling special championship T-shirts for a cost of $7 each.

GRAPH

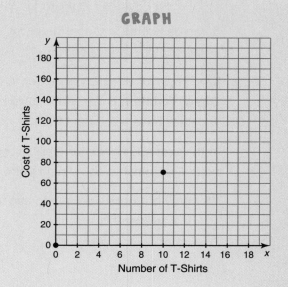

MULTIPLE REPRESENTATIONS

TABLE

Number of T-shirts	Cost in Dollars

EQUATION

Let *y* represent:

Let *x* represent:

When the y-intercept is (0, 0), the equation can be written in a simpler form.

It can be written in the form $y = kx$, with $k \neq 0$. No addition or subtraction for the y-intercept value is needed.

When a linear equation is written in this form, the variables x and y show *direct variation*. **Direct variation** is the relationship between two quantities x and y such that the two variables have a constant ratio.

In the example from your graphic organizer, the equation is $y = 7x$. The ratio $\frac{y}{x} = 7$ is true regardless of what coordinate point in the table is used.

5. Why is it not necessary to use the formula $\frac{y_2 - y_1}{x_2 - x_1}$ to determine the rate of change of this relation?

6. How can you tell from the graph if an equation shows a direct variation?

Be prepared to share your solutions and methods.

SLOPE-INTERCEPT FORM

3.6

Determining the Rate of Change and *y*-Intercept

Learning Goals

In this lesson, you will:

▶ Graph lines using the slope and *y*-intercept.

▶ Calculate the *y*-intercept of a line when given the slope and one point that lies on the line.

▶ Write equations of lines in slope-intercept form if given two points that lie on the line or the slope and one point that lies on the line.

▶ Write equations in point-slope form if given the slope and one point that lies on the line.

▶ Graph lines in standard form by using the intercepts.

▶ Convert equations from point-slope form and standard form to slope-intercept form.

▶ Discuss the advantages and disadvantages of point-slope and standard form.

Key Terms

▶ point-slope form

▶ standard form

3

A synonym is a word that has the same or almost the same definition of another word. An example of synonyms is "prefer" and "like." In many cases, journalists use synonyms if their writing has many words that repeat within an article or a blog. Sometimes, synonyms can also make an awkwardly written article read more smoothly. Of course, literary critics may sometimes criticize a writer for using too complex synonyms when more common words could easily be used. Can you think of other advantages and disadvantages for using synonyms?

Problem 1   Using Slope-Intercept Form to Graph a Line

As you learned previously, the slope-intercept form of a linear equation is $y = mx + b$ where m is the slope of the line. However, you did not learn what b represented. In the slope-intercept form, b is the y-intercept of the line. Remember that the slope of the line is the "steepness" of that line.

Douglas is giving away tickets to a concert that he won from a radio station contest. Currently, he has 10 tickets remaining. He gives a pair of tickets to each person who asks for them.

An equation to represent this context is:

y = number of tickets available
x = number of people who request tickets
$y = -2x + 10$

> Notice the equation is written in slope-intercept form.

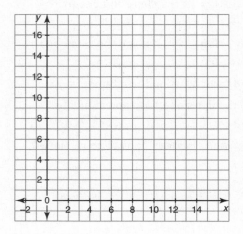

Follow these steps to graph the equation:

Step 1: Write the coordinates for the y-intercept.

Step 2: Plot the y-intercept on the coordinate plane shown.

Step 3: Write the slope as a ratio.

Step 4: Use the slope and count from the y-intercept. To identify another point on the graph, start at the y-intercept and count either down (negative) or up (positive) for the rise. Then, count either left (negative) or right (positive) for the run.

Continue the counting process to plot the next points.

Step 5: Connect the points to make a straight line.

Graph each line. Be careful to take into account the scales on the axes.

1. $y = \dfrac{3}{2}x - 1$

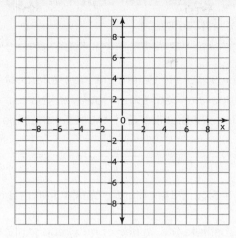

First think about the *y*-intercept and then interpret the slope.

2. $y = \dfrac{-5}{2}x + 3$

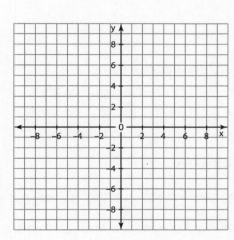

3

3. $y = 10x + 25$

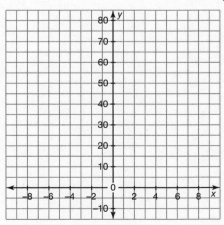

How will you know by the equation if your graph will go up to the right or down to the right?

Problem 2   Using Slope-Intercept Form to Calculate the y-Intercept

So far, you have been able to determine the y-intercept of a line when given the linear equation in the slope-intercept form. However, you can determine the y-intercept of a line when given the slope of that line and one point that lies on the line.

Given: $m = \frac{-3}{2}$ and the point (4, 5) that lies on the line.

Step 1: Substitute the values of m, x, and y into the *equation for a line* $y = mx + b$. The x- and y-values are obtained from the point that is given.

$$y = mx + b$$
$$5 = \frac{-3}{2}(4) + b$$

Step 2: Solve the equation for b.

$$5 = -6 + b$$
$$5 + 6 = -6 + b + 6$$
$$11 = b$$

The slope of the line is 11.

Calculate the y-intercept of each line when given the slope and one point that lies on the line.

1. $m = 9$; (2, 11)

2. $m = 2.25$; (16, −52)

3. $m = \frac{-3}{8}$; (50, 7)

Can you estimate where the line will cross the y-axis, based on the slope and one point?

Problem 3   Using Slope-Intercept Form to Write Equations of Lines

So far, you have determined the *y*-intercept from the slope-intercept form of a linear equation, and the *y*-intercept from the slope and a point on that lies on the line given. Now, you will write the equation of a line when given two points that lie on the line.

Given: Points (15, −13) and (5, 27) that lie on a line.

Step 1: Calculate the slope using $\dfrac{y_2 - y_1}{x_2 - x_1}$.

$$\frac{27 - (-13)}{5 - 15} = \frac{40}{-10} = \frac{-4}{1} = -4$$

Step 2: Calculate the *y*-intercept by using the slope and one of the points.

$$y = mx + b$$
$$27 = -4(5) + b$$
$$27 = -20 + b$$
$$27 + 20 = -20 + b + 20$$
$$47 = b$$

Step 3: Substitute *m* and *b* into the equation $y = mx + b$.

$$y = mx + b$$
$$y = -4x + 47$$

The equation for a line in which points (15, −13) and (5, 27) lie on that line is $y = -4x + 47$.

So, this time you have to calculate the slope first.

Write an equation of a line using the given information. Show your work.

1. (7, 15) and (−39, −8)

2. (429, 956) and (249, 836)

3. (6, 19) and (0, −35)

4. The slope is -8. The point $(3, 12)$ lies on the line.

Problem 4 Another Form of a Linear Equation

Let's develop a second form of a linear equation.

Step 1: Begin with the formula for slope.

$$m = \frac{y_2 - y_1}{x_2 - x_1}$$

Step 2: Rewrite the equation to remove the fraction by multiplying both sides of the equation by $(x_2 - x_1)$.

$$m(x_2 - x_1) = \left(\frac{y_2 - y_1}{x_2 - x_1}\right)(x_2 - x_1)$$

Step 3: After simplifying, the result is:

$$m(x_2 - x_1) = (y_2 - y_1)$$

Step 4: Remove the subscripts for the second point.

$$m(x - x_1) = (y - y_1)$$

The formula $m(x - x_1) = (y - y_1)$ is the **point-slope form** of a linear equation that passes through the point (x_1, y_1) and has slope m.

Step 5: Finally, substitute the values for m, x, and y into the point-slope form of the equation. The x- and y-values should be substituted in for x_1 and y_1.

1. Write the equation of a line in point-slope form with a slope of -8 and the point (3, 12) that lies on the line.

2. While this equation took little time to write, it is difficult to visualize its graph or even its y-intercept. To determine the y-intercept, manipulate the equation using algebra to write the equation in $y = mx + b$ form. Show all work.

3. What is the y-intercept of this line?

4. Write the equation of each line in point-slope form. Then, state the y-intercept of the line. Show all work.

   a. slope $= -5$; (16, 32) lies on the line

   b. $m = \frac{2}{3}$; (9, -18) lies on the line

c. rate of change is -4.5; $(-80, 55)$ lies on the line

5. What are the advantages and disadvantages of using point-slope form?

Problem 5   Exploring Standard Form of a Linear Equation

Tickets for the school play cost $5.00 for students and $8.00 for adults. On opening night, $1600 was collected in ticket sales.

This situation can be modeled by the equation $5x + 8y = 1600$. You can define the variables as shown.

$$x = \text{number of student tickets sold}$$
$$y = \text{number of adult tickets sold}$$

This equation was not written in slope-intercept form. It was written in *standard form*.

The **standard form** of a linear equation is $Ax + By = C$, where A, B, and C are constants and A and B are not both zero.

1. Explain what each term of the equation represents in the problem situation.

2. What is the independent variable? What is the dependent variable? Explain your reasoning.

Remember, the x-intercept crosses the x-axis so the value of y is 0. The y-intercept crosses the y-axis so the value of x is 0.

3. Calculate the x-intercept and y-intercept for this equation. Show your work.

4. What are the meanings of the x-intercept and y-intercept?

5. Use the *x*-intercept and *y*-intercept to graph the equation of the line.

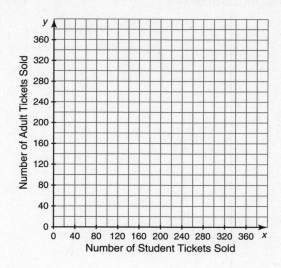

6. What is the slope of this line? Show your work.

7. What does the slope mean in this problem situation?

8. If 100 student tickets were sold, how many adult tickets were sold? Show your work.

Talk the Talk

1. Match each graph with the correct equation written in standard form. Show your work and explain your reasoning.

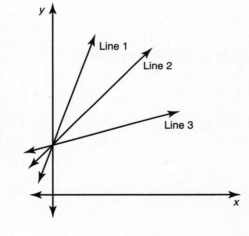

Notice that there are no values on the x- and y-axis. What strategies can you use to determine which graph goes with which equation?

a. $3x - 12y = -60$

b. $6x - 2y = -10$

c. $9x - 9y = -45$

a.

b.

c.

2. What are the advantages and disadvantages of using standard form?

 Be prepared to share your solutions and methods.

3

Chapter 3 Summary

Key Terms

- rate (3.1)
- rate of change (3.1)
- per (3.1)
- unit rate (3.1)
- rise (3.1)

- run (3.1)
- $\frac{\text{rise}}{\text{run}}$ (3.1)
- first differences (3.2)
- slope (3.4)
- slope-intercept form (3.4)

- y-intercept (3.5)
- direct variation (3.5)
- point-slope form (3.6)
- standard form (3.6)

3.1 Using Rise over Run to Calculate the Rate of Change from a Graph

Rate of change is a phrase used when a rate is used to describe a rate of increase (or decrease) in a real-life situation. A unit rate is a rate which has a denominator of 1 unit.

The ratio $\frac{\text{rise}}{\text{run}}$ is a representation of the rate of change shown in a graph.

Example

Choose two points on the graph that can be read without estimation.

Point A (1, 45) and point B (3, 135)

The rise is the vertical change from the first point to the second point. The rise is 90 miles.

The run is the horizontal change from the first point to the second point. The run is 2 hours.

$$\frac{\text{rise}}{\text{run}} = \frac{90 \text{ miles}}{2 \text{ hours}}$$

The unit rate is $\frac{45 \text{ miles}}{1 \text{ hour}}$.

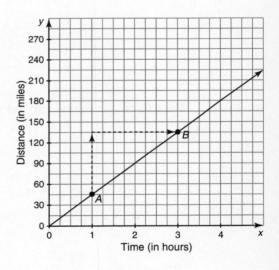

3.2 Determining Rate of Change from a Table

There is a formal mathematical process that can be used to calculate the rate of change of a linear relation from a table of values with at least two coordinate pairs.

The rate of change of a linear relation is $\dfrac{y_2 - y_1}{x_2 - x_1}$, where the first point is at (x_1, y_1), and the second point is at (x_2, y_2).

Example

Two points are chosen from the table of values and labeled as shown.

$$(x_1, y_1) = (3, 3.75)$$

$$(x_2, y_2) = (5, 6.25)$$

Number of Raffle Tickets	Total Cost of Raffle Tickets (in dollars)
3	3.75
5	6.25
7	8.75
9	11.25

Substitute the values into the formula.

$$\frac{y_2 - y_1}{x_2 - x_1} = \frac{6.25 - 3.75}{5 - 3}$$

$$= \frac{2.5}{2}$$

$$= \frac{1.25}{1}$$

The unit rate is $\dfrac{\$1.25}{1 \text{ ticket}}$.

3.3 Determining Rate of Change from a Context

A context representing a linear function often provides enough information to determine the rate of change of the function.

Example

Joelle is selling fruit smoothies at a summer festival. During the first two days of the festival, Joelle sells 120 smoothies. By the conclusion of the four-day event, Joelle had sold an additional 88 smoothies.

$$120 \text{ smoothies} + 88 \text{ smoothies} = 208 \text{ smoothies total}$$

$$\frac{208 \text{ smoothies}}{4 \text{ days}} = \frac{52 \text{ smoothies}}{1 \text{ day}}$$

The unit rate is $\frac{52 \text{ smoothies}}{1 \text{ day}}$.

3.4 Determining Rate of Change from an Equation

Slope is another mathematical term for rate of change. If a linear equation is solved for y, the coefficient of x represents the rate of change, or slope of the line. An equation in this form, $y = mx + b$, where m is the slope of the line, is said to be in slope-intercept form.

Example

A slope of a line can be determined for the equation $15y - 6x = 30$.

$$15y - 6x = 30$$
$$15y = 6x + 30$$
$$y = \frac{6}{15}x + 2$$
$$y = \frac{2}{5}x + 2$$

The equation is now in slope-intercept form. The slope of the line, m, is $\frac{2}{5}$.

3.5 Determining the y-Intercept of a Linear Equation

The *y*-intercept is the *y*-coordinate of the point where a graph crosses the *y*-axis.
The *y*-intercept can also be written as the coordinate pair (0, *y*).

Example

To determine the *y*-intercept from the equation $2x + 6y = 24$, substitute $x = 0$ into the
equation and solve for *y*.

$$2x + 6y = 24$$
$$2(0) + 6y = 24$$
$$6y = 24$$
$$y = 4$$

The *y*-intercept is (0, 4).

3.6 Using Slope-Intercept Form to Graph a Line

The slope-intercept form of a linear equation is $y = mx + b$, where *m* is the slope of the
line and *b* is the *y*-intercept of the line. An equation in this form provides all the information
necessary to graph the line representing the equation.

Example

A sketch of a graph can be created for
the equation

$$y = -\frac{2}{3}x + 6.$$

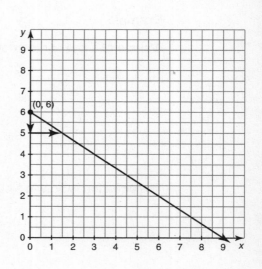

From the equation, it is known that the
y-intercept is (0, 6). Plot this point on
the graph.

From the equation, it is known that the slope
is $-\frac{2}{3}$. Use the slope and count from the
y-intercept to graph another point on the line.
Finally, connect the points.

3.6 Using the Point-Slope Form of a Linear Equation

The point-slope form of a linear equation that passes through the point (x_1, y_1) and has slope m is $m(x - x_1) = (y - y_1)$.

Example

An equation can be written for a line with a slope of $-\frac{5}{6}$ which goes through the point $(12, -8)$.

$$m(x - x_1) = (y - y_1)$$

$$-\frac{5}{6}(x - 12) = (y - (-8))$$

$$-\frac{5}{6}x + 10 = y + 8$$

$$-\frac{5}{6}x + 2 = y$$

$$y = -\frac{5}{6}x + 2$$

3

3.6 Using the Standard Form of a Linear Equation

The standard form of a linear equation is $Ax + By = C$, where A, B, and C are constants and A and B are not both zero.

Example

The y-intercept and the x-intercept can be calculated for the linear equation $4x + 2y = 16$ in standard form.

Sketch the graph of the line.

$$4x + 2y = 16$$
$$4(0) + 2y = 16$$
$$2y = 16$$
$$y = 8$$

The y-intercept is at $(0, 8)$.

$$4x + 2y = 16$$
$$4x + 2(0) = 16$$
$$4x = 16$$
$$x = 4$$

The x-intercept is at $(4, 0)$.

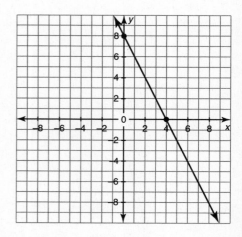

Now you're on to bigger and better things!

4 MULTIPLE REPRESENTATIONS OF LINEAR FUNCTIONS

You probably see people jogging or running in your neighborhood all the time. Jogging regularly helps keep your heart and lungs healthy, helps to strengthen your immune system, reduces stress, and can even improve your mood!

4

WILLIE CATCHEM

Analyzing Problem Situations Using Multiple Representations

Learning Goal

In this lesson, you will:

▶ Analyze problem situations using multiple representations.

A triathlon is a race that involves three different challenges—swimming, cycling, and running. In the Ironman triathlon, competitors must swim for 3.8 kilometers, cycle for 180 kilometers, and run for 42.2 kilometers.

All together, the Ironman triathlon is over 140 miles long! That's about the same distance to drive from Portland, Oregon, to Tacoma, Washington. Can you estimate a location on a map that is about 140 miles from where you live? How long do you think it would take you to swim, ride, and run from your house to that location?

4

Problem 1   Through the Origin

Willie Catchem is a long-distance runner. His training includes running about 240 kilometers per week. Willie's training route goes by Kevin's house at the beginning of his run. Willie also runs past Kevin's house near the end of his run.

One day Kevin wanted to determine how fast Willie actually ran. Kevin knows that Willie's complete running route is 12 kilometers.

The table shows Willie's times.

Time (min)	Distance (km)
0	0
40	12

1. Calculate Willie's average speed in kilometers per minute.

   Average speed =

2. Define variables for the time and distance Willie runs.

3. Write an equation that shows the relationship between these variables.

4. If Willie ran for 15 minutes and he maintains his average speed, how far would he run?

5. Willie often runs 10K (10-kilometer) races. How long would it take for Willie to finish a 10K race if he runs at his average speed?

There are about 6.2 miles in a 10K race.

6. Complete the table using the information from Questions 1 through 5.

Time (min)	Distance from Kevin's House (km)
0	
15	
	10
	12

7. Graph the points on the coordinate plane shown.

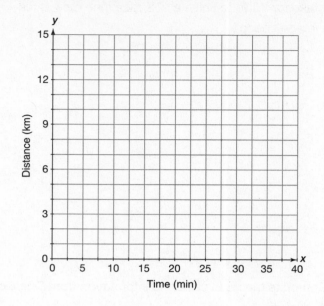

8. Does it make sense to connect the points for this problem situation? Why or why not?

9. Describe the type of function represented.

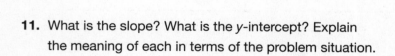

To determine the type of function consider the shape of the graph and where it crosses the y-axis.

10. Which is the independent variable? Which is the dependent variable?

11. What is the slope? What is the *y*-intercept? Explain the meaning of each in terms of the problem situation.

12. If it takes Willie 18 minutes to get to Kevin's house from his own house, how far away is Willie's house?

Problem 2   A Different Intercept

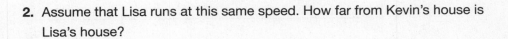

Lisa runs the same route as Willie, but her house is in between Willie's and Kevin's houses. Lisa uses her watch to clock her running time, using Kevin's house as her marker. The table shows the watch readings each time she passes Kevin's house.

Time (min)	Distance from Kevin's House (km)
8.5	0
47.25	12

The first time shown is not 0 minutes. How will that change the problem?

1. Calculate Lisa's average speed in kilometers per minute.

Average speed =

2. Assume that Lisa runs at this same speed. How far from Kevin's house is Lisa's house?

3. Define variables for the time it takes Lisa to run from her house, and her distance from Kevin's house.

4. Write an equation that shows the relationship between the variables.

5. If Lisa started at her house and ran for 10 minutes and maintains her average speed during her run, how far would she be from Kevin's house?

6. If Lisa is 6 kilometers past Kevin's house, how long has she been running since she left home?

7. Use the points and the information you have about Lisa's time running to complete the table.

Time from Her House (min)	Distance from Kevin's House (km)
0	
10	
	6

8. Graph the points on the coordinate plane shown.

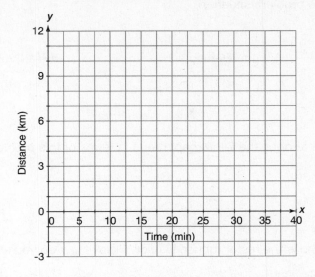

9. Does it make sense to connect the points in this problem situation? Why or why not?

10. Describe the type of function represented.

How does the function representing Lisa's average speed compare to the function representing Willie's average speed?

11. Which is the independent variable? Which is the dependent variable?

12. Marty claims that the slope for the problem situation is −2.635 and the y-intercept is 0.31. Samantha doesn't think that Marty is correct. Using only the graph you created, who is correct? Explain your reasoning.

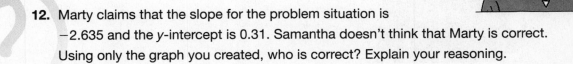

13. What is the slope? What is the *y*-intercept? Explain the meaning of each in terms of the problem situation.

14. What does the *y*-intercept mean in terms of this problem situation?

15. Who is the faster runner, Lisa or Willie? How do you know?

How did each representation, the scenario, table, graph, and equation, help you determine who was the faster runner?

Be prepared to share your solutions and methods.

PONY EXPRESS

Interpreting the Standard Form of a Linear Equation

Learning Goals

In this lesson, you will:

▶ Use the standard form of a linear equation to represent a problem situation.

▶ Use the standard form to analyze and solve problems.

▶ Identify the meaning and value of the component expressions in the standard form of a linear equation.

I n 1860, the Pony Express began as a way to deliver the news and mail faster. It consisted of relays of men riding horses carrying saddlebags of mail across a 2000-mile trail. The service started on April 3, 1860, when riders left simultaneously from St. Joseph, Missouri, and Sacramento, California. The first westbound trip was made in 9 days and 23 hours, and the eastbound journey in 11 days and 12 hours. Eventually, the Pony Express had more than 100 stations, 80 riders, and between 400 and 500 horses.

The express route was very dangerous, but only one mail delivery was ever lost. The service lasted only until the completion of the Pacific Telegraph line, which made communicating much quicker than mail. Although California relied upon news from the Pony Express during the early days of the Civil War, the horse line never made much money. In fact, the founders of the Pony Express had to file for bankruptcy. However, the romantic drama surrounding the Pony Express has made it a part of the legend of the American West. Can you think of other ways people also communicated before the U.S. Postal Service or email?

Problem 1   The Stagecoach and the Pony Express

In the mid-1800s, delivering mail and news across the American Great Plains was time-consuming and made for a long delay in getting vital information from one side of the country to the other. At the time, most mail and news traveled by stagecoach along the main stagecoach lines at about 8 miles per hour. The long stretch of 782 miles from the two largest cities on either side of the plains, St. Louis, Missouri, and Denver, Colorado, was a very important part of this trail.

1. Use the variable x for the time that a stagecoach was driven in hours, and write an expression to represent the distance the stagecoach was driven in miles.

2. How many miles would the stagecoach travel in:
   a. 8 hours?

   b. 10 hours 30 minutes?

3. In how many hours would the stagecoach travel:
   a. 200 miles?

   b. 150 miles?

4. How long would it take the stagecoach to travel from St. Louis to Denver?

5. The Pony Express riders averaged about 10.7 miles per hour. Use the variable y for the time that the Pony Express rider rides in hours. Then, write an expression to represent the distance that he rides in miles.

6. How many miles would the rider travel in:

    a. 7 hours?

    b. 11 hours 15 minutes?

7. In how many hours would the rider travel:

    a. 100 miles?

b. 600 miles? (hours and minutes)

8.

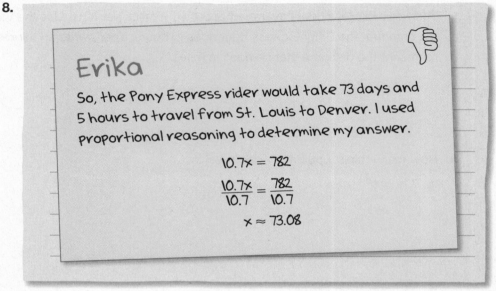

Erika

So, the Pony Express rider would take 73 days and 5 hours to travel from St. Louis to Denver. I used proportional reasoning to determine my answer.

$$10.7x = 782$$

$$\frac{10.7x}{10.7} = \frac{782}{10.7}$$

$$x \approx 73.08$$

Explain to Erika why her calculation is incorrect and determine the correct answer.

Problem 2 What If Both Were Used?

What operation do you use to show the combination of these methods?

Sometimes the mail may have been delivered using a stagecoach for part of the route and the Pony Express for the remainder of the route.

1. Write an expression for the distance that was traveled using both of these delivery methods on one trip.

2. Write an equation that represents using this method to deliver the mail from St. Louis to Denver.

3. If the Pony Express rode for 20 hours from St. Louis before handing off the mail to a stagecoach, how long would it take the stagecoach to get the mail to Denver?

4

4. If the stagecoach traveled for 50 hours from St. Louis before handing off the mail to a Pony Express rider, how long would it take the rider to get the mail to Denver?

Do your answers make sense? Did you check your work?

5. Complete the table.

Delivery Time of Mail Between St. Louis and Denver

Time the Mail Was in a Stagecoach (hours)	Time the Mail Was with the Pony Express (hours)
	20
50	
	50
8	
	7
	56.07

6. Graph the points from the table on the coordinate plane and label the axes.

Delivery Time of Mail Between St. Louis and Denver

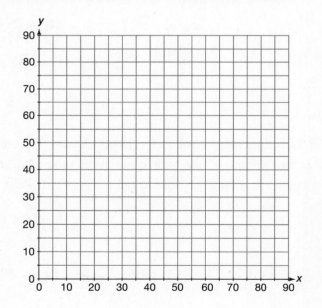

7. Describe the points on the graph.

8. Does it make sense to connect the points in this problem situation? Why or why not?

9. Based on this graph, describe the type of function represented by this equation.

10. Analyze the table and graph you completed.

    a. As the *x*-value increases, what happens to the *y*-value?

    b. As the *y*-value increases, what happens to the *x*-value?

Problem 3   The Parts

1. If the Pony Express took the mail for 400 miles, how many miles would the stagecoach need to travel to complete the trip from St. Louis to Denver?

2. How much time would it take for the stagecoach to finish this trip?

3. If the stagecoach took the mail for 300 miles, how many miles would the Pony Express rider need to complete the trip from St. Louis to Denver?

4. How much time would it take for the rider to finish this trip?

Your equation $8x + 10.7y = 782$ is in the standard form of a linear equation, $ax + by = c$, where a, b, and c are constants.

5. What are the values of a, b, and c in the equation you wrote for mail deliveries between stagecoaches and the Pony Express?

6. Describe what each constant, variable, or other expression represents in this equation.

   a. x

   b. y

   c. $8x$

   d. $10.7y$

   e. $8x + 10.7y$

   f. 782

7. Describe the meaning of each in this problem situation.

   a. x-intercept

   b. y-intercept

 Be prepared to share your solutions and methods.

4

4.3

SLOPES, FORMS, GRAPHS, AND INTERCEPTS

Connecting the Standard Form with the Slope-Intercept Form of Linear Functions

Learning Goals

In this lesson, you will:

▶ Graph linear functions in standard form.

▶ Transform linear functions from one form to the other.

▶ Determine the slope and the intercepts of linear equations in standard form.

Many different kinds of animals can change their form to help them avoid or ward off predators. Some chameleons can change color to camouflage themselves so that predators don't see them. When threatened, a frill-necked lizard can raise up and expand the skin around its neck to make it look more dangerous.

But the vampire squid has one of the most unusual ways of changing form when it feels threatened. A vampire squid will literally turn itself inside out!

You have done a lot of work with changing form in mathematics—but hopefully not because you were threatened! What ways have you changed from one form to another in math?

Problem 1 Exploring Linear Equations in Standard Form

 Complete the table for each linear equation shown in standard form. Use the *x*- or *y*-value given to determine the unknown value. Use the third column to show your work.

1. $4x + 3y = 12$

x	y	Work
2		
	5	
−2		

2. $5x - 4y = 20$

x	y	Work
6		
	−4	
0		

3. $3x - 5y = 30$

x	y	Work
0		
	0	
−3		

4. Plot the points from the tables to graph each equation on the coordinate plane.

Label each line with its equation.

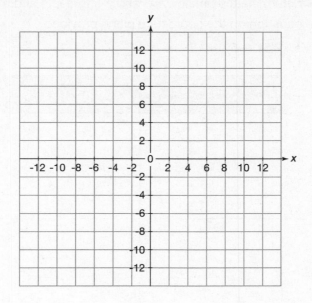

5. Use two points from each table to calculate the slope for each equation.

a. $4x + 3y = 12$

$m =$

Check out your graphs to get a sense of each slope before you use the slope formula. Which graphs will have a positive slope? Which graphs will have a negative slope?

b. $5x - 4y = 20$

$m =$

c. $3x - 5y = 30$

$m =$

6. Complete the table by using the equation in standard form and the given value to determine the unknown x- and y-intercepts and a third point. Then, graph the equation on the coordinate plane provided.

a. $2.5x + 5y = 15$

x	y	Work
0		
	0	
−1		

x-intercept:

y-intercept:

Slope: $m =$

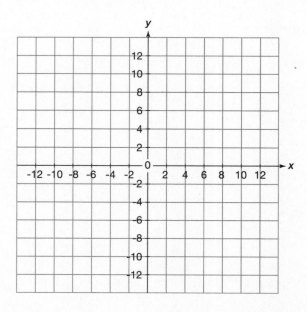

b. $\frac{2}{3}x - 6y = 12$

x	y	Work
0		
	0	

x-intercept:

y-intercept:

Slope: $m =$

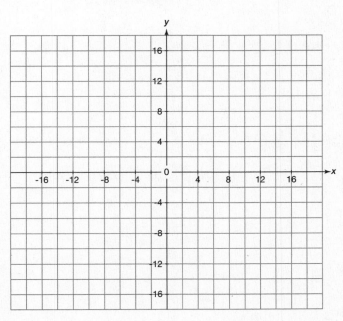

7. Using the information from Question 6, rewrite each linear function in slope-intercept form.

I prefer standard form when I am looking for the *x*- and *y*-intercepts.

Standard Form	Slope-Intercept Form
$2.5x + 5y = 15$	
$\frac{2}{3}x - 6y = 12$	

I prefer slope-intercept form. I can tell what the slope is and what the *y*-intercept is just by looking at the equation.

4

Problem 2   Transform from One to the Other

To convert a linear function in standard form to slope-intercept form, solve for y.

1. Rewrite each equation in standard form to slope-intercept form.

a. $4x + 8y = 12$

b. $2.5x - 3.5y = 7$

c. $\frac{3}{4}x + \frac{1}{3}y = 7$

d. $11x - 25y = 185$

e. $ax - by = c$

This equation shows how you can determine the slope and y-intercept even in a standard form equation.

To convert a linear equation in slope-intercept form to standard form, solve for the constant term.

2. Rewrite each equation in standard form.

a. $y = 3x - 7$

b. $y = \frac{3}{4}x - \frac{7}{5}$

4

c. $y = -3.5x + 7.8$

Now I see how to write any slope-intercept form equation in standard form.

d. $y = mx + b$

Talk the Talk

Describe how to determine the slope, *y*-intercept, and *x*-intercept from each form of an equation.

1. $y = mx + b$

slope:

y-intercept:

x-intercept:

2. $ax + by = c$

slope:

y-intercept:

x-intercept:

4

Be prepared to share your solutions and methods.

4.4

THE JOURNEY STARTS WITH A SINGLE STEP—BUT THERE ARE MANY STEPS AFTER THAT!

Intervals of Increase, Decrease, and No Change

Learning Goals

In this lesson, you will:

▶ Analyze a problem situation using multiple representations.

▶ Identify intervals of increase, decrease, and constant values of a function.

Key Terms

▶ increasing function
▶ constant function
▶ decreasing function
▶ interval of increase
▶ interval of decrease
▶ constant interval

4

Overland travel is a long journey often traveling between countries. Overland traveling can involve traveling by train, bus, bike, or boat, but never by plane. People often travel with a group for weeks or months to get to their destinations. Some of the longest overland travel routes are in Africa. The Cairo to Cape Town route covers more than 10,000 kilometers and follows the Nile River through a number of African countries. This journey can take up to 4 months to complete! Some people have even overland traveled from London to South Africa. How long do you think that journey would take? Would you want to go on an overland travel journey?

Problem 1 Heading to the Basketball Courts

James is visiting at Tyler's house about 2000 feet from home. He then decides to head to the park to play basketball. From Tyler's house, James walks at the rate of 8 feet per second and it takes him 25 minutes to arrive at the basketball courts.

1. How far away from home is James when he arrives at the basketball courts?

About how many miles is 2000 feet?

2. Define variables for the time that James walks in seconds, and his distance in feet from home.

3. Write an equation that relates these variables.

4. What is the slope and the y-intercept of this function? Explain what each represents in this problem situation.

5. Complete the table to select appropriate upper and lower bounds to graph this function.

Remember, when setting the lower and upper bounds think about how to surround the data.

Quantity	Lower Bound	Upper Bound	
Time			
Distance			

6. What is the domain of this problem situation? What is the range?

7. Graph the function and label each axis.

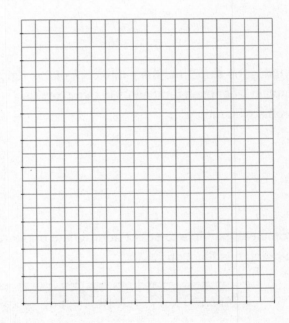

8. As the time increases, what happens to the distance?

When both values of a function increase, the function is said to be an **increasing function.**

Problem 2   Shooting Hoops

James arrives at the park and has one hour to play basketball.

1. How far is James from home?

2. After being at the park for 20 minutes, how far is James from home? How far is James from home after 1 hour?

3. Use the same variables for the time since James has left Tyler's house in seconds, and his overall distance from home in feet. Write an equation that relates these variables for this situation.

Can I write this equation in slope-intercept form?

4. What is the slope and the y-intercept of this function? Explain what each represents in terms of this problem situation.

5. Complete the table to select appropriate upper and lower bounds to graph this function.

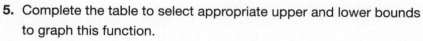

Quantity	Lower Bound	Upper Bound
Time		
Distance		

6. What is the domain of this problem situation? What is the range?

7. Graph the function and label each axis.

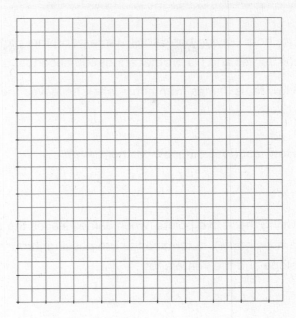

8. Describe the graph of this function.

9. Which value does not change but remains constant?

When the *y*-value does not change or remains constant, the function is called a **constant function.**

Problem 3 Heading for Home

After an hour playing basketball, James's brother picks him up and drives him home. It takes James and his brother about 600 seconds to get home.

1. How far is James from home when he leaves the basketball courts?

2. How fast does James's brother drive?

3. Using these two points (when James leaves the basketball courts and when he arrives home), determine the line passing through these points by calculating the slope and the *y*-intercept.

> Will the slope be positive or negative now that he is heading back home?

4. What is the slope and the *y*-intercept of this function?

5. Select appropriate upper and lower bounds to graph this function.

Quantity	Lower Bound	Upper Bound
Time		
Distance		

6. What is the domain of this problem situation? What is the range?

7. Graph the function and label each axis.

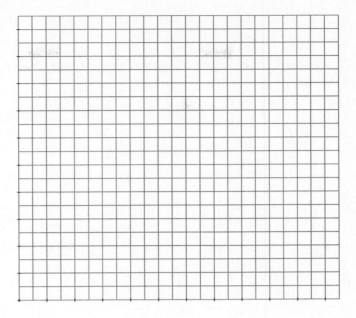

8. As the time increases, what happens to the distance?

When the value of a dependent variable decreases as the independent variable increases, the function is said to be a **decreasing function**.

Problem 4   The Whole Journey

You have just written equations and graphed the separate parts of James's walk to the park from Tyler's house, his time playing basketball at the park, and his car ride home. Let's consider all three parts of his journey away from home as one function and graph.

1. Select appropriate upper and lower bounds to graph his journey as one function on the coordinate plane.

Quantity	Lower Bound	Upper Bound
Time		
Distance		

2. What is the domain of James' journey? The range?

3. Graph all three functions as one function and label each axis.

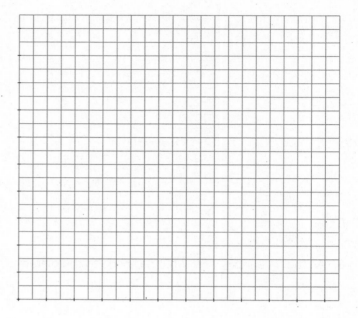

4. Label the parts of the function that are increasing, decreasing, or constant. Explain your reasoning.

5. For which values of time is the function increasing?

How do the rates compare in each segment of the graph?

6. For which values of time is the function decreasing?

7. For which values of time is the function constant?

You can describe the intervals of a function by analyzing what happens at specific independent values.

- When a function is increasing for some values of the independent variable, it is said to have an **interval of increase.**
- When a function is decreasing for some values of the independent variable, it is said to have an **interval of decrease.**
- When a function is constant for some values of the independent variable, it is said to have a **constant interval.**

Problem 5   Analyzing Different Functions

1. Complete the table and graph the function $y = |x + 2|$.

x	y
−6	
−4	
−2	
0	
2	
5	

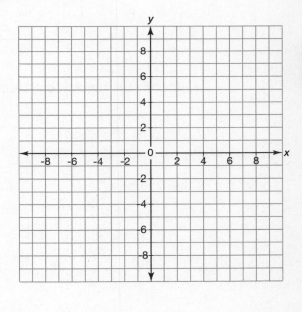

2. Identify the intervals of increase and decrease for this function.

3. Complete the table and graph the function $y = -|x - 2|$.

x	y
−6	
−4	
−2	
0	
2	
4	
5	

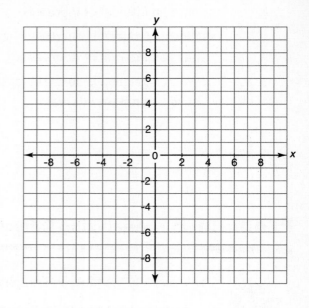

4. Identify the intervals of increase and decrease for this function.

Be prepared to share your solutions and methods.

4.5 PIECEWISE FUNCTIONS

Developing the Graph of a Piecewise Function

Learning Goals

In this lesson, you will:

▶ Develop the graph of a piecewise function from a context with or without a table of values.

▶ Represent a piecewise function algebraically by using appropriate notation, equations, and their domains.

▶ Graph piecewise functions from contexts with or without diagrams.

▶ Physically model the graphs of piecewise functions using technology.

Key Term

▶ piecewise function

The fairy tale *Hansel and Gretel* tells the story of a brother and sister who become lost in the woods and find a house made of candy. As the two children begin eating the candy house, a witch, who lives in the house, captures them and keeps them hostage in order to eat them.

As the story goes, the children left a trail of breadcrumbs from their home and into the woods so that they could find their way back. What similarities and differences are there between this trail of breadcrumbs and the kinds of graphs you have been creating? Create a graph showing a trail of breadcrumbs. How will you label the axes?

Problem 1 Investigating a Line

1. Suppose you earn $48 helping your neighbor with yard work. You think that you will spend $3 of your earnings each day.

   a. How much money will you have left after 3 days? Show your work.

   b. How much money will you have left after 5 days? Show your work.

   c. How much money will you have left after 10 days? Show your work.

2. Complete the table to show the amounts of money you will have left for different numbers of days.

Time since You Started Spending (days)	Amount of Money Left (dollars)
0	
1	
2	
3	
4	
5	

3. Write an equation that represents the amount of money you have left in terms of the number of days since you started spending your earnings. Be sure to tell what each variable in your equation represents.

4. Use the coordinate plane to create a graph of your equation. Make sure to choose your bounds and intervals first. Label your graph clearly. Do not forget to name your graph. Extend your graph to show when your amount of earnings left would be 0.

Variable Quantity	Lower Bound	Upper Bound	Interval

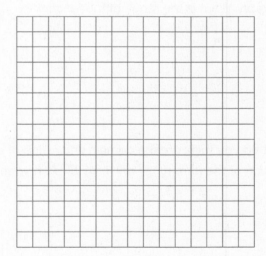

5. Determine the *x*- and *y*-intercepts of the graph. Explain what they mean in terms of the problem situation.

6. Is the slope of your line positive or negative? Does this make sense in terms of the problem situation?

7. Consider your linear function without considering the problem situation. You can determine the domain of your linear function by using your graph.

   a. What is the domain of the function?

Recall that the set of all possible input values of a function is the domain of the function and the set of all possible output values is the range of the function.

   b. You can also determine the range by using your graph. What is the range of the function?

8. What do you think are the domain and range of any linear function of the form $f(x) = mx + b$? Explain your reasoning.

9. Now consider your linear function again in terms of the problem situation.

    a. What is the domain of the linear function in the problem situation? Explain your reasoning.

    b. What is the range of the linear function in the problem situation? Explain your reasoning.

Problem 2　Representing a Piecewise Function

Suppose that you do not spend the $48 by spending $3 each day. Instead, after 5 days of spending $3 each day, you do not spend anything for 5 days. You then spend $1.50 each day.

1. Complete the table to show the amounts of money you will have left for different numbers of days.

Time Since You Started Spending (days)	Amount of Earnings Left (dollars)
0	
1	
2	
3	
4	
5	
6	
7	
8	
9	
10	
11	
12	
13	

2. Use the coordinate plane to create a graph from the table of values. Make sure to choose your bounds and intervals first. Label your graph clearly. Extend your graph to show when your amount of earnings left would be 0.

Variable Quantity	Lower Bound	Upper Bound	Interval

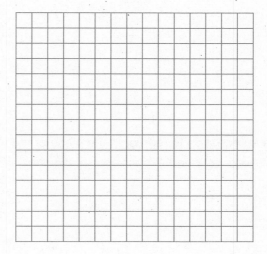

The graph that you created in Question 2 represents a *piecewise function*. A **piecewise function** is a function whose equation changes for different parts, or pieces, of the domain.

3. What is the domain of this function in the problem situation?

4. How many pieces make up this function? (How many different equations are needed to describe this function?)

5. What is the domain of each piece?

6. Write an equation to represent the piece of the function from 0 days to 5 days. Show your work and explain how you determined your answer.

7. Write an equation to represent the piece of the function from 6 days to 10 days. Show your work and explain your reasoning.

8. Write an equation to represent the piece of the function from 11 days to 32 days. Show your work and explain your reasoning.

Recall, function notation can be used to write functions such that the dependent variable is replaced with the name of the function, such as $f(x)$.

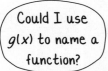

Could I use $g(x)$ to name a function?

9. Complete the definition of your piecewise function, $f(x)$. For each piece of the domain, write the equation you wrote in Questions 6, 7, and 8.

$$f(x) = \begin{cases} \rule{3cm}{0.4pt}, & 0 \leq x \leq 5 \\ \rule{3cm}{0.4pt}, & 5 < x \leq 10 \\ \rule{3cm}{0.4pt}, & 10 < x \leq 32 \end{cases}$$

10. Which piece should you use to determine the *x*-intercept? Which piece should you use to determine the *y*-intercept?

11. Determine the intercepts of the graph. Show all your work.

12. When will you run out of money? How does this compare to the number of days it would take you to run out of money in Problem 1?

Problem 3 Modeling a Piecewise Function

1. Every Tuesday and Thursday, once Kurt gets home from school, he changes his clothes and goes to the community center, which is 1.9 miles from his house, to lift weights. He leaves his house at 3:25 pm and jogs at a steady rate for one mile to his friend Moe's house, which is on the way to the community center. He stops and has a 10-minute break at Moe's house, and then they walk at a consistent pace the rest of the way to the center. They arrive at the center at 4:10 pm.

   a. Draw a graph on the grid provided that could show Kurt's trip from home to the community center. Make sure to label the axes and show the intervals. Do not forget to name your graph.

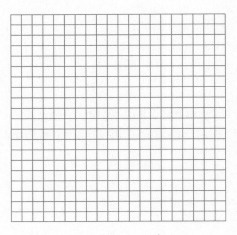

   b. Label the three pieces of the graph X, Y, and Z from left to right.

   c. Order the pieces in terms of their slopes, from least to greatest. Explain why you chose to order the pieces in that matter.

2. Lucy and her friends are hiking from their campsite to a waterfall. They leave their camp at 6:00 AM. They normally hike at a rate of 3 miles per hour, but on steeper parts of the hike, they slow down to 2 miles per hour. They have a one-hour picnic lunch by the waterfall and then reverse their path and hike back to the campsite.

The diagrams shown provide information about the trail that they will be hiking. The diagrams are not drawn to scale.

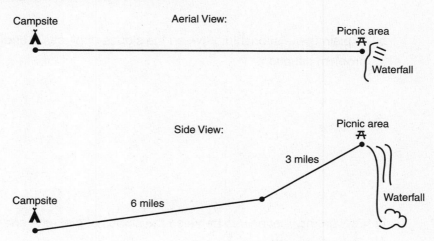

a. Draw a graph modeling Lucy's hiking trip. Label the axes "Time of Day" and "Distance from Campsite." Make sure to show the intervals on the grid and do not forget to name your graph.

4

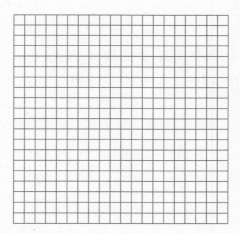

b. Label the pieces of the graph *A*, *B*, *C*, *D*, and *E* from left to right.

3. Examine your graph.

   a. What pieces have negative slopes? Why are these slopes negative?

   b. Explain the relationship between the slopes of pieces *B* and *D* in terms of the problem situation.

   c. Explain the relationship between the slopes of pieces *A* and *B* in terms of the problem situation.

   d. Why is the slope of piece *A* greater than the slope of piece *B* in the graph, but in the diagram the reverse is true?

   e. Draw a vertical line through the graph to demonstrate its symmetry. Explain why there is symmetry in the graph.

Problem 4 Acting Out a Piecewise Function

You will need a graphing calculator, a Calculator-Based Ranger (CBR), and a connector cable for this activity. You will also need a meter stick and masking tape to mark off distance measures.

Graphs of piecewise functions representing people walking, with time on the *x*-axis and distance on the *y*-axis, are shown after the step-by-step instructions. Your goal is to act out the graph by walking in the way that matches the graph. As you do this, your motion will be plotted alongside the graph to monitor your performance.

Step 1: Prepare the workspace.

  ● Clear an area at least 1 meter wide and 4 meters long in front of a wall.

  ● From the wall, measure the distances of 0.5, 1, 1.5, 2, 2.5, 3, 3.5, and 4 meters. Mark these distances on the floor using masking tape.

Step 2: Prepare the technology.

  ● Connect the CBR to a graphing calculator.

  ● Transfer the RANGER program from the CBR to the calculator. This only needs to be done the first time. It will then be stored in your calculator.

  ● Press **2nd** | **LINK** | ⟶ | **ENTER** |.

  ● Open the CBR and press the appropriate button on it for the type of calculator you are using. Your calculator screen will display RECEIVING and then DONE. The CBR will flash a green light and beep.

Step 3: Access the RANGER program.

  ● Press | **PRGM** | for program. Choose RANGER. Press | **ENTER** |.

  ● Press | **ENTER** | to display the MAIN MENU.

  ● Choose **APPLICATIONS** . Choose **METERS** .

  ● Choose **MATCH** or **DISTANCE** **MATCH** .

  ● Press | **ENTER** |. A graph will be displayed.

Step 4: Act out the graph.

- Examine the graph. Plan your path. Use the scale to gauge where to begin in relation to the wall. Will you walk toward or away from the wall? Will you walk fast or slow?

- Hold the graphing calculator in one hand and the RANGER in the other hand. The lid of the RANGER should be aimed toward the wall.

- Press | **ENTER** |. Begin walking in a manner that matches the graph. Use the scale and floor markings as guides. You will hear a clicking sound and see a green light as your motion is plotted alongside the piecewise graph on the graphing calculator.

- When the time is finished, examine your performance. What changes should you make?

- Press | **ENTER** | to display the OPTIONS menu. Choose **SAME MATCH** .

- Press | **ENTER** | and try the walk a second time.

- Continue acting out walks by pressing | **ENTER** | and **NEW MATCH**.

- When finished, press | **ENTER** |, choose **MAIN MENU** , and **QUIT** .

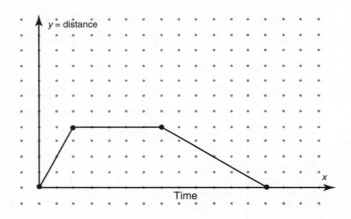

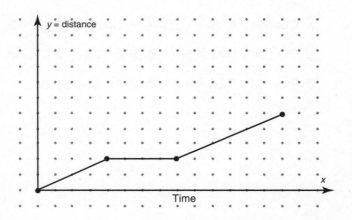

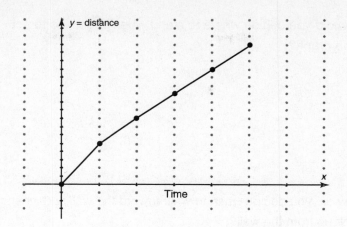

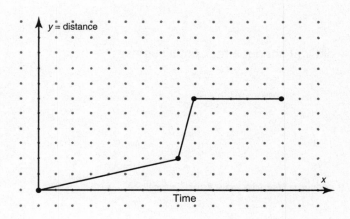

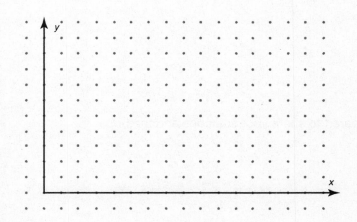

1. How did you decide where to stand when beginning to act out a graph?

Did this activity help you make sense of the graphs?

2. How did you decide when to walk toward the wall and when to back up from the wall?

3. How did you act out a horizontal segment?

4. How did you decide how fast to walk?

Be prepared to share your solutions and methods.

Chapter 4   Summary

Key Terms

▶ increasing function (4.4)

▶ constant function (4.4)

▶ decreasing function (4.4)

▶ interval of increase (4.4)

▶ interval of decrease (4.4)

▶ constant interval (4.4)

▶ piecewise function (4.5)

4.1 Analyzing Problem Situations Using Multiple Representations

A problem situation can be represented multiple ways.

Example

Natalie is biking around a small park. The table shows the time it took Natalie to complete one lap around the park on the 1.8 mile bike path.

Time (minutes)	Distance (miles)
0	0
10	1.8

The calculation of Natalie's average speed in miles per minute is shown.

$$\text{Average speed} = \frac{1.8 \text{ miles}}{10 \text{ minutes}}$$

$$= 0.18 \text{ mile per minute}$$

Natalie's average speed is 0.18 mile per minute.

Next, an equation is shown to represent the relationship between the time and distance Natalie bikes. The first step is to define the variables and what they represent.

Let t represent to the time Natalie bikes.

Let d represent to the distance Natalie bikes.

$d = 0.18t$

Once the variables are defined and an equation is determined, substitution can be used to determine how far Natalie can ride in 45 minutes.

$$d = 0.18t$$
$$d = 0.18(45)$$
$$d = 8.1$$

If Natalie bikes for 45 minutes, she will bike 8.1 miles.

Finally, a graph shows the relationship between the time and distance Natalie biked.

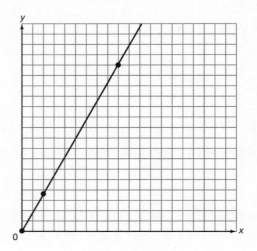

4.2 Interpreting the Standard Form of a Linear Equation

A problem situation can be represented with the standard form of a linear equation.

Example

Maria is baking muffins from scratch for the school bake sale. It takes Maria 1.25 hours to bake each batch of muffins.

An expression can be written to represent the amount of time it takes Maria to bake a certain number of batches of muffins.

> Let x equal the number of muffin batches Maria bakes.
> The expression $1.25x$ equals the amount of time it takes Maria to bake x batches of muffins.

Once a variable is defined and an expression is determined, it can be determined how long it takes Maria to bake batches of muffins. For example, substitution is used to determine how long it takes Maria to bake 3 batches of muffins.

$$1.25x = 1.25(3)$$
$$= 3.75$$

It would take Maria 3.75 hours to bake 3 batches of muffins.

Isabel is baking pre-made frozen muffins for the school bake sale. It takes Isabel 0.75 hour to bake each batch of muffins.

As with Maria, an expression can be written to represent the amount of time it takes Isabel to bake a certain number of batches of muffins.

Let y equal the number of muffin batches Isabel bakes.

The expression $0.75y$ equals the amount of time it takes Isabel to bake y batches of muffins.

Once the variable is defined and an expression is determined, substitution will determine how many batches of muffins Isabel can bake in a certain amount of hours.

$$0.75y = 3$$
$$\frac{0.75y}{0.75} = \frac{3}{0.75}$$
$$y = 4$$

Isabel could bake 4 batches of muffins in 3 hours.

Supposed Maria and Isabel had to take turns sharing the school kitchen to bake the muffins. The school kitchen is available for 10 hours. An equation in standard form can be written to represent this situation.

$$1.25x + 0.75y = 10$$

Using the equation and substitution, it can be determined how many batches of muffins Isabel can bake when Maria bakes 4 batches.

$$1.25x + 0.75y = 10$$
$$1.25(4) + 0.75y = 10$$
$$5 + 0.75y = 10$$
$$0.75y = 5$$
$$y \approx 6.7$$

If Maria bakes 4 batches of muffins, Isabel can bake 6 batches of muffins in the time allotted.

4.3 Determining the Slope and Intercepts of a Linear Equation in Standard Form

The standard form of a linear equation can be used to determine the *x*-intercept, the *y*-intercept, and the slope of the graph of the linear equation.

Example

Use the standard form of the linear equation to determine the *x*-intercept, the *y*-intercept, and the slope of the graph of the linear equation.

$$2x + 3y = 18$$

To determine the *y*-intercept, solve the equation when $x = 0$.

$$2x + 3y = 18$$
$$2(0) + 3y = 18$$
$$3y = 18$$
$$y = 6$$

The *y*-intercept is (0, 6).

To determine the *x*-intercept, solve the equation when $y = 0$.

$$2x + 3y = 18$$
$$2x + 3(0) = 18$$
$$2x = 18$$
$$x = 9$$

The *x*-intercept is (9, 0).

The slope can be calculated from the intercepts.

$$m = \frac{0 - 6}{9 - 0}$$
$$= \frac{-6}{9}$$
$$= -\frac{2}{3}$$

The slope is $-\frac{2}{3}$.

4.3 Converting Linear Equations between Standard Form to Slope-Intercept Form

To convert a linear equation in standard form to slope-intercept form, solve for y.
To convert a linear equation in slope-intercept form to standard form, solve for the constant term.

Example

To convert the linear equation $3x + 4y = 48$ to slope-intercept form, follow the steps shown.

$$3x + 4y = 48$$
$$4y = -3x + 48$$
$$y = -\frac{3}{4}x + 12$$

To convert the linear equation $y = \frac{3}{5}x + 2$ to standard form, follow the steps shown.

$$y = \frac{3}{5}x + 2$$
$$5y = 3x + 10$$
$$-3x + 5y = 10$$

4.4 Identifying Functions as Increasing, Decreasing, or Constant

When both the value of the independent variable and the value of the dependent variable of a function increase, the function is said to be an increasing function. When the value of the dependent variable does not change or remains constant as the value of the independent variable increases, the function is called a constant function. When the value of the dependent variable decreases as the value of the independent variable increases, the function is said to be a decreasing function.

Example

The graph of $y = 3x + 1$ is shown.

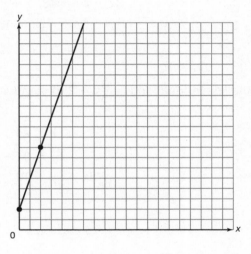

The independent variable increases, the dependent variable increases. The function is an increasing function.

Mental activities, like puzzles and even math problems, can improve and increase your brain function. You wouldn't want your brain function to be constant or decreasing!

The graph of $y = -\frac{1}{2}x + 7$ is shown.

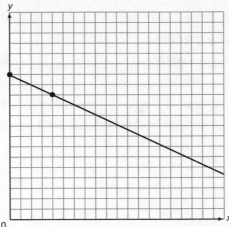

The independent variable increases, the dependent variable decreases. The function is a decreasing function.

The graph of $y = 6$ is shown.

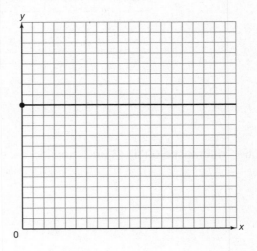

The independent variable increases, the dependent does not change or remains constant. The function is a constant function.

4.4 Identifying Intervals of Increase, Decrease, and Constant Values of a Function

When a function is increasing for some values of the independent variable, it is said to have an interval of increase. When a function is decreasing for some values of the independent variable, it is said to have an interval of decrease. When a function is constant for some values of the independent variable, it is said to have a constant interval.

Example

The graph of $y = |x + 3|$ is shown.

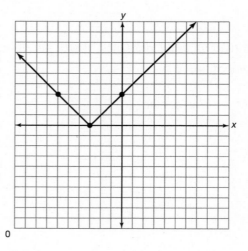

The function decreases until -3 and then increases after -3.

4.5 Writing a Piecewise Function from a Table or Context

Piecewise functions can be used to model any situation with varying rates of change.
A piecewise function represents more than one function, each of which corresponds to a
part of the domain. Use the slope and a point from a problem situation to determine each
part of the function. Write the function using x to represent a number from the domain of
the function f. Use the left brace symbol "{" to show that all expressions in the group are
part of the function.

Example

Hour	Toys Painted
0	0
1	6
3	18
4	24
5	24
6	29
9	44

$$f(x) = \begin{cases} 6x, & 0 \le x \le 4 \\ 24, & 4 < x \le 5 \\ 5x - 1, & 5 < x \le 9 \end{cases}$$

4

4.5 Graphing a Piecewise Function from a Table, Context, or Diagram

The graph of a piecewise function may consist of a series of line segments with different slopes. It can be generated from a table, an algebraic representation, or a context with or without a diagram. Graph each section of the piecewise function on the same graph with the appropriate bounds and intervals.

Example

Salvador starts painting toys at 8:00 AM. He steadily paints 6 toys per hour until his lunch break at 12:00 PM. He gets back to work an hour later and paints at a rate of 5 toys per hour until his shift is over at 5:00 PM.

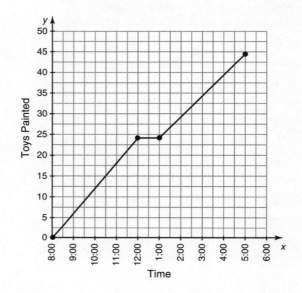

5 THE REAL NUMBER SYSTEM

Pi is probably one of the most famous numbers in all of history. As a decimal, it goes on and on forever without repeating. Mathematicians have already calculated trillions of the decimal digits of pi. It really is a fascinating number. And it's delicious!

5

5.1 IS IT A BIRD OR A PLANE?
Rational Numbers

Learning Goals

In this lesson, you will:

▶ Use a number line to compare and order rational numbers.

▶ Learn about types of numbers and their properties.

▶ Perform operations with rational numbers.

Key Terms

▶ natural numbers (counting numbers)

▶ whole numbers

▶ integers

▶ closed

▶ rational numbers

There are all kinds of different numbers, which have been given some strange names. It seems that mathematicians can come up with an infinite number of different kinds of numbers.

A repunit number is an integer with all 1's as digits. So, 11, 111, and so on, are all repunit numbers. Pronic numbers are numbers that are the products of two consecutive numbers. The numbers 2, 6, and 12 are the first pronic numbers ($1 \times 2 = 2$, $2 \times 3 = 6$, and $3 \times 4 = 12$).

To find the numbers that some call "lucky" numbers, first start with all the counting numbers (1, 2, 3, 4, and so on). Delete every second number. This will give you 1, 3, 5, 7, 9, 11, and so on. The second number in that list is 3, so cross off every third number remaining. Now you have 1, 3, 7, 9, 13, 15, 19, 21, and so on. The next number that is left is 7, so cross off every seventh number remaining.

Can you list all the "lucky" numbers less than 50?

Problem 1   A Science Experiment

Your science class is conducting an experiment to see how the weight of a paper airplane affects the distance that it can fly. Your class is divided into two groups. Group 1 uses a yard stick to measure the distances that an airplane flies, and Group 2 uses a meter stick. Group 2 then takes their measurements in meters and converts them to feet. The results of the experiment are shown in the table.

> Because paper is typically sold in 500-sheet quantities, a paper's weight is determined by the weight of 500 sheets of the paper. So, 500 sheets of 20-pound paper weighs 20 pounds.

Type of Paper	Group 1 Measurements	Group 2 Converted Measurements
20-pound paper	$13\frac{7}{8}$ feet	13.9 feet
28-pound paper	$14\frac{3}{8}$ feet	14.4 feet

1. Your science class needs to compare the Group 1 measurement to the Group 2 converted measurement for each type of paper.

   a. Write $13\frac{7}{8}$ as a decimal.   b. Write $14\frac{3}{8}$ as a decimal.

2. On the number line shown, graph the Group 1 measurements written as decimals and the Group 2 converted measurements.

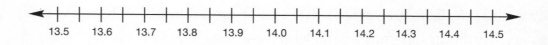

13.5   13.6   13.7   13.8   13.9   14.0   14.1   14.2   14.3   14.4   14.5

3. Use the number line to determine which group's flight traveled farther for the 20-pound paper and for the 28-pound paper. Write your answers using complete sentences.

Problem 2 Natural Numbers, Whole Numbers, and Integers

1. The first set of numbers that you learned when you were very young was the set of *counting numbers*, or *natural numbers*. **Natural numbers** consists of the numbers that you use to count objects: {1, 2, 3, 4, 5, ...}.

   In the set {1, 2, 3, 4, 5, ...} the dots at the end of the list mean that the list of numbers goes on without end.

   a. How many counting numbers are there?

   b. Does it make sense to ask which counting number is the greatest? Explain why or why not.

   c. Why do you think this set of numbers is called the natural numbers?

You have also used the set of *whole numbers*. **Whole numbers** are made up of the set of natural numbers and the number 0, the additive identity.

2. Why is zero the additive identity?

3. Other than being used as the additive identity, how else is zero used in the set of whole numbers?

4. Explain why having zero makes the set of whole numbers more useful than the set of natural numbers.

Another set of numbers is the set of **integers**, which is a set that includes all of the whole numbers and their additive inverses.

5. What is the additive inverse of a number?

6. Represent the set of integers. Remember to use three dots to show that the numbers go on without end in both directions.

> Use brackets to represent sets.

7. Does it make sense to ask which integer is the least or which integer is the greatest? Explain why or why not.

When you perform operations such as addition or multiplication on the numbers in a set, the operations could produce a defined value that is also in the set. When this happens, the set is said to be **closed** under the operation.

The set of integers is said to be closed under the operation of addition. This means that for every two integers a and b, the sum $a + b$ is also an integer.

8. Are the natural numbers closed under addition? Write an example to support your answer.

9. Are the whole numbers closed under addition? Write an example to support your answer.

10. Consider the operation of subtraction. Are the natural numbers closed under subtraction? Write an example to support your answer.

11. Are the whole numbers closed under subtraction? Write an example to support your answer.

12. Are the integers closed under subtraction? Write an example to support your answer.

13. Are any of these sets closed under multiplication? Write examples to support your answers.

14. Are any of these sets closed under division? Write examples to support your answer.

You have learned about the additive inverse, the multiplicative inverse, the additive identity, and the multiplicative identity.

15. Which of these does the set of natural numbers have, if any? Explain your reasoning.

16. Which of these does the set of whole numbers have, if any? Explain your reasoning.

17. Which of these does the set of integers numbers have, if any? Explain your reasoning.

Problem 3 Rational Numbers

1. A **rational number** is a number that can be written in the form $\frac{a}{b}$, where a and b are both integers and b is not equal to 0.

a. Does the set of rational numbers include the set of whole numbers? Write an example to support your answer.

b. Does the set of rational numbers include the set of integers? Write an example to support your answer.

c. Does the set of rational numbers include all fractions? Write an example to support your answer.

d. Does the set of rational numbers include all decimals? Write an example to support your answer.

2. Is the set of rational numbers closed under addition? Write an example to support your answer.

3. Is the set of rational numbers closed under subtraction? Write an example to support your answer.

4. Is the set of rational numbers closed under multiplication? Write an example to support your answer.

5. Is the set of rational numbers closed under division? Write an example to support your answer.

6. Does the set of rational numbers have an additive identity? Write an example to support your answer.

7. Does the set of rational numbers have a multiplicative identity? Write an example to support your answer.

8. Does the set of rational numbers have an additive inverse? Write an example to support your answer.

9. Does the set of rational numbers have a multiplicative inverse? Write an example to support your answer.

10. You can add, subtract, multiply, and divide rational numbers in much the same way that you did using integers. Perform the indicated operation.

a. $1.5 + (-8.3) =$

b. $-12.5 - 8.3 =$

Remember, it is a good idea to estimate first!

c. $-\dfrac{1}{2} - \dfrac{3}{4} =$

d. $2\dfrac{1}{2} + \left(-3\dfrac{7}{8}\right) =$

e. $-2.0 \times (-3.6) =$

f. $6.75 \times (-4.2) =$

g. $-\dfrac{2}{3} \times \dfrac{3}{8} =$

h. $-3\dfrac{3}{4} \times \left(-2\dfrac{3}{5}\right) =$

i. $-1.5 \div 4.5 =$

j. $-2.1 \div (-3.5) =$

k. $-\dfrac{2}{5} \div \dfrac{3}{10} =$

l. $-1\dfrac{3}{8} \div \left(-2\dfrac{2}{5}\right) =$

Be prepared to share your solutions and methods.

5.2

SEW WHAT?
Irrational Numbers

Learning Goals

In this lesson, you will:

▶ Identify decimals as terminating or repeating.

▶ Write repeating decimals as fractions.

▶ Identify irrational numbers.

Key Terms

▶ irrational number

▶ terminating decimal

▶ repeating decimal

▶ bar notation

In 2006, a 60-year-old Japanese man named Akira Haraguchi publicly recited the first 100,000 decimal places of π from memory.

The feat took him 16 hours to accomplish—from 9 a.m. on a Tuesday morning to 1:30 a.m. the next day.

Every one to two hours, Haraguchi took a break to use the restroom and have a snack. And he was videotaped throughout the entire process—to make sure he didn't cheat!

5

Problem 1　Repeating Decimals

You have worked with some numbers like π that are not rational numbers. For example, $\sqrt{2}$ and $\sqrt{5}$ are not the square roots of perfect squares and cannot be written in the form $\frac{a}{b}$, where a and b are both integers.

Even though you often approximate square roots using a decimal, most square roots are *irrational numbers*. Because all rational numbers can be written as $\frac{a}{b}$ where a and b are integers, they can be written as *terminating decimals* (e.g. $\frac{1}{4} = 0.25$) or *repeating decimals* (e.g., $\frac{1}{6} = 0.1666...$). Therefore, all other decimals are **irrational numbers** because these decimals cannot be written as fractions in the form $\frac{a}{b}$ where a and b are integers and b is not equal to 0.

1. Convert the fraction to a decimal by dividing the numerator by the denominator. Continue to divide until you see a pattern.

   $\frac{1}{3} = \quad 3\overline{)1}$

2. Describe the pattern that you observed in Question 1.

3. Convert each fraction to a decimal by dividing the numerator by the denominator. Continue to divide until you see a pattern.

   a. $\frac{5}{6} = 6\overline{)5}$ b. $\frac{2}{9} = 9\overline{)2}$

   c. $\frac{9}{11} = 11\overline{)9}$ d. $\frac{3}{22} = 22\overline{)3}$

4. Explain why these decimal representations are called repeating decimals.

A **terminating decimal** is a decimal that has a last digit. For instance, the decimal 0.125 is a terminating decimal because $\frac{125}{1000} = \frac{1}{8}$. 1 divided by 8 is equal to 0.125.

A **repeating decimal** is a decimal with digits that repeat in sets of one or more. You can use two different notations to represent repeating decimals. One notation shows one set of digits that repeat with a bar over the repeating digits. This is called **bar notation**.

$$\frac{1}{3} = 0.\overline{3} \qquad\qquad \frac{7}{22} = 0.3\overline{18}$$

Another notation shows two sets of the digits that repeat with dots to indicate repetition. You saw these dots as well when describing the number sets in the previous lesson.

$$\frac{1}{3} = 0.33... \qquad\qquad \frac{7}{22} = 0.31818...$$

5. Write each repeating decimal from Question 2 using both notations.

   a. $\frac{5}{6} =$ **b.** $\frac{2}{9} =$

   c. $\frac{9}{11} =$ **d.** $\frac{3}{22} =$

Some repeating decimals represent common fractions, such as $\frac{1}{3}$, $\frac{2}{3}$, and $\frac{1}{6}$, and are used often enough that you can recognize the fraction by its decimal representation. For most repeating decimals, though, you cannot recognize the fraction that the decimal represents. For example, can you tell which fraction is represented by the repeating decimal 0.44... or $0.\overline{09}$?

You can use algebra to determine the fraction that is represented by the repeating decimal 0.44... . First, write an equation by setting the decimal equal to a variable that will represent the fraction.

$$w = 0.44...$$

Next, write another equation by multiplying both sides of the equation by a power of 10. The exponent on the power of 10 is equal to the number of decimal places until the decimal begins to repeat. In this case, the decimal begins repeating after 1 decimal place, so the exponent on the power of 10 is 1. Because $10^1 = 10$, multiply both sides by 10.

$$10w = 4.4...$$

Then, subtract the first equation from the second equation.

$$10w = 4.44...$$
$$\underline{-w = 0.44...}$$
$$9w = 4$$

Finally, solve the equation by dividing both sides by 9.

6. What fraction is represented by the repeating decimal 0.44...?

7. Complete the steps shown to determine the fraction that is represented by $0.\overline{09}$.

8. Repeat the procedure above to write the fraction that represents each repeating decimal.

    a. 0.55... =

    b. 0.0505... =

    c. $0.\overline{12}$ =

    d. $0.\overline{36}$ =

Problem 2   Sewing a Tablecloth

Your aunt wants to sew a round tablecloth with lace trim. The diameter of the tablecloth must be 70 inches. Your aunt wants to know how much trim to purchase.

Remember that the formula for the circumference of a circle is $C = \pi d$ or $C = 2\pi r$.

1. What number should your aunt multiply the diameter of the tablecloth by in order to know how many inches of lace trim to purchase?

Earlier, you used an approximation of the number π to determine the circumference of a circle. Even though you used this approximation, the number π is a decimal with a never-ending number of digits that do not repeat.

Another irrational number is $\sqrt{6}$.

2. Use a calculator to calculate each power.

   $2.1^2 =$ $2.2^2 =$ $2.3^2 =$

   $2.4^2 =$ $2.5^2 =$ $2.6^2 =$

3. Which of the bases above must $\sqrt{6}$ be between?

4. Continue the process in Question 2 for the hundredths place.

   $2.41^2 =$ $2.42^2 =$ $2.43^2 =$

   $2.44^2 =$ $2.45^2 =$ $2.46^2 =$

5. Continue the process above for the thousandths place.

   $2.445^2 =$ $2.446^2 =$ $2.447^2 =$

   $2.448^2 =$ $2.449^2 =$ $2.450^2 =$

6. Determine $\sqrt{6}$ using the calculator. Do you see any digits repeating in a pattern?

7. What can you conclude about the square roots of numbers that are not perfect squares? Explain your reasoning.

 Be prepared to share your solutions and methods.

WORTH 1000 WORDS

5.3 Real Numbers and Their Properties

Learning Goals

In this lesson, you will:

▶ Classify numbers in the real number system.

▶ Understand the properties of real numbers.

Key Terms

▶ real number

▶ Venn diagram

▶ closure

The word *zero* has had a long and interesting history so far. The word comes from the Hindu word *sunya*, which meant "void" or "emptiness." In Arabic, this word became *sifr*, which is also where the word *cipher* comes from. In Latin, it was changed to *cephirum*, and finally, in Italian it became *zevero* or *zefiro*, which was shortened to *zero*.

The ancient Greeks, who were responsible for creating much of modern formal mathematics, did not even believe zero was a number!

5

Problem 1 Picturing the Real Numbers

Combining the set of rational numbers and the set of irrational numbers produces the set of **real numbers**. You can use a **Venn diagram** to represent how the sets within the set of real numbers are related. Look at the rectangles on the next page and follow the steps shown.

The Venn diagram was introduced in 1881 by John Venn, British philosopher and mathematician.

1. First, at the top of the large rectangle, write the label "Real Numbers." This entire rectangle represents the set of real numbers.

2. Label the smaller rectangle at the right "Irrational Numbers."

3. Label the top of the smaller rectangle at the left "Rational Numbers."

4. Inside the rectangle that represents rational numbers, draw a large circle. Inside the circle, at its top, write the label "Integers."

5. Inside the circle that represents integers, draw a smaller circle. Inside the circle, at its top, write the label "Whole Numbers."

6. Inside the circle that represents the whole numbers, draw a smaller circle. Inside this circle, write the label "Natural Numbers." Your Venn diagram that represents the real number system is complete.

7. Use your Venn diagram to decide whether each statement is true or false. Explain your reasoning.

   a. A whole number is sometimes an irrational number.

   b. A real number is sometimes a rational number.

   c. A whole number is always an integer.

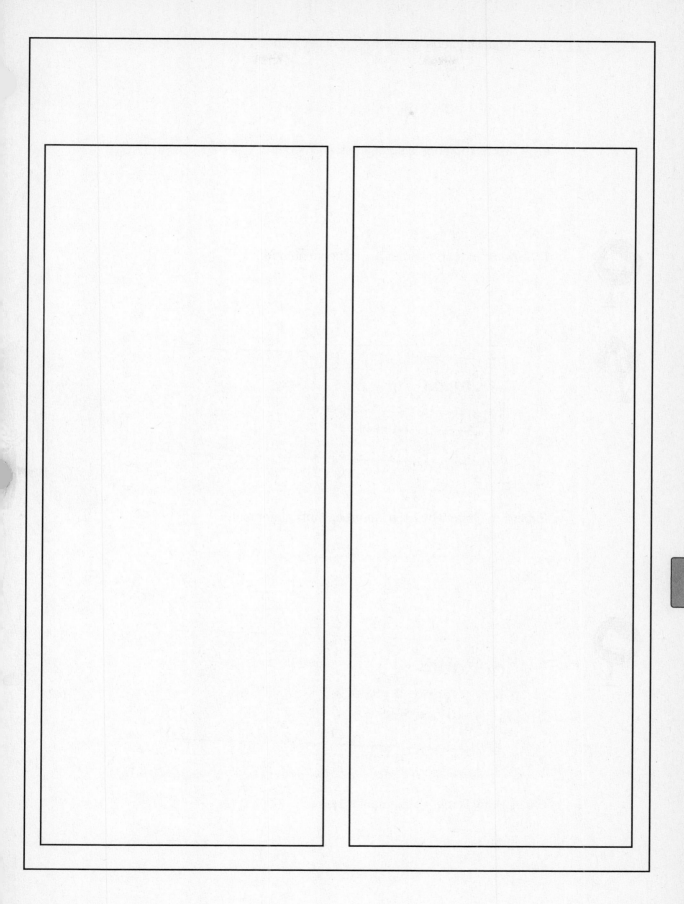

d. A negative integer is always a whole number.

e. A rational number is sometimes an integer.

f. A decimal is sometimes an irrational number.

8.

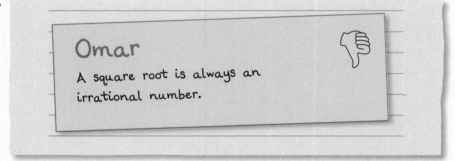

Omar

A square root is always an irrational number.

Explain to Omar why he is incorrect in his statement.

9.

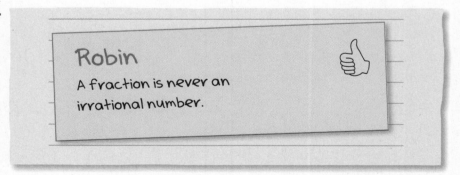

Robin

A fraction is never an irrational number.

Explain why Robin's statement is correct.

Problem 2 Properties of Real Numbers

The real numbers, together with their operations and properties, form the real number system. You have already encountered many of the properties of the real number system in various lessons. Let's review these properties.

Closure: A set of numbers is said to be closed under an operation if the result of the operation on two numbers in the set is a defined value also in the set. For instance, the set of integers is closed under addition. This means that for every two integers a and b, the sum $a + b$ is also an integer.

1. Is the set of real numbers closed under addition? Write an example to support your answer.

2. Is the set of real numbers closed under subtraction? Write an example to support your answer.

3. Is the set of real numbers closed under multiplication? Write an example to support your answer.

4. Is the set of real numbers closed under division? Write an example to support your answer.

Additive Identity: An additive identity is a number such that when you add it to a second number, the sum is equal to the second number.

5. For any real number a, is there a real number such that $a + $ (the number) $= a$? What is the number?

6. Does the set of real numbers have an additive identity? Write an example to support your answer.

Multiplicative Identity: A multiplicative identity is a number such that when you multiply it by a second number, the product is equal to the second number.

7. For any real number a, is there a real number such that $a \times$ (the number) $= a$? What is the number?

8. Does the set of real numbers have a multiplicative identity? Write an example to support your answer.

Additive Inverse: Two numbers are additive inverses if their sum is the additive identity.

9. For any real number a, is there a real number such that $a +$ (the number) $= 0$? What is the number?

10. Does the set of real numbers have an additive inverse? Write an example to support your answer.

You have been using these properties for a long time, moving forward you now know that they hold true for the set of real numbers.

Multiplicative Inverse: Two numbers are multiplicative inverses if their product is the multiplicative identity.

11. For any real number a, is there a real number such that $a \times$ (the number) $= 1$? What is the number?

12. Does the set of real numbers have a multiplicative inverse? Write an example to support your answer.

Commutative Property of Addition: Changing the order of two or more addends in an addition problem does not change the sum.

For any real numbers a and b, $a + b = b + a$.

13. Write an example of the property.

Commutative Property of Multiplication: Changing the order of two or more factors in a multiplication problem does not change the product.

For any real numbers a and b, $a \times b = b \times a$.

14. Write an example of the property.

Associative Property of Addition: Changing the grouping of the addends in an addition problem does not change the sum.

For any real numbers a, b and c, $(a + b) + c = a + (b + c)$.

15. Write an example of the property.

Associative Property of Multiplication: Changing the grouping of the factors in a multiplication problem does not change the product.

For any real numbers a, b, and c, $(a \times b) \times c = a \times (b \times c)$.

16. Write an example of the property.

Reflexive Property of Equality:

For any real number a, $a = a$.

17. Write an example of the property.

Symmetric Property of Equality:

For any real numbers a and b, if $a = b$, then $b = a$.

18. Write an example of the property.

The Transitive Property of Equality:

For any real numbers a, b, and c, if $a = b$ and $b = c$, then $a = c$.

19. Write an example of the property.

Talk the Talk

For each problem, identify the property that is represented.

1. $234 + (-234) = 0$

2. $-4 \times (3 \times 5) = (-4 \times 3) \times 5$

3. $-24 \times 1 = -24$

4. $-67 \times 56 = 56 \times (-67)$

5. $-456 + 34 = 34 + (-456)$

6. $4 \times 0.25 = 1$

7. If $5 = (-1)(-5)$ then $(-1)(-5) = 5$.

8. If $c = 5 \times 7$ and $35 = 70 \div 2$, then $c = 70 \div 2$.

9. $a + (4 + c) = (a + 4) + c$

10. $\left(-\dfrac{3}{4}\right)\left(-\dfrac{4}{3}\right) = 1$

11. $-2\dfrac{3}{4} \times 1 = -2\dfrac{3}{4}$

12. $\left(-\dfrac{3}{4}\right) + \left(\dfrac{4}{3} + 5\right) = \left(-\dfrac{3}{4} + \dfrac{4}{3}\right) + 5$

Be prepared to share your solutions and methods.

Chapter 5 Summary

Key Terms

▶ natural numbers (counting numbers) (5.1)

▶ whole numbers (5.1)

▶ integers (5.1)

▶ closed (5.1)

▶ rational numbers (5.1)

▶ irrational number (5.2)

▶ terminating decimal (5.2)

▶ repeating decimal (5.2)

▶ bar notation (5.2)

▶ real number (5.3)

▶ Venn diagram (5.3)

▶ closure (5.3)

Properties

▶ Additive Identity (5.3)

▶ Multiplicative Identity (5.3)

▶ Additive Inverse (5.3)

▶ Multiplicative Inverse (5.3)

▶ Commutative Property of Addition (5.3)

▶ Commutative Property of Multiplication (5.3)

▶ Associative Property of Addition (5.3)

▶ Associative Property of Multiplication (5.3)

▶ Reflexive Property of Equality (5.3)

▶ Symmetric Property of Equality (5.3)

▶ Transitive Property of Equality (5.3)

5.1 Comparing and Ordering Rational Numbers Using a Number Line

Fractions and decimals can be compared and ordered by converting fractions to decimals and plotting on a number line.

Example

The number line is used to show $5\frac{5}{16} > 5.3$. The fraction $5\frac{5}{16}$ is equal to 5.3125.

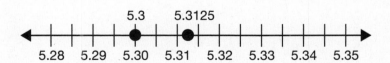

5.1 Performing Operations with Rational Numbers

A rational number is a number that can be written in the form $\frac{a}{b}$, where a and b are both integers and b is not equal to 0. You can add, subtract, multiply, and divide rational numbers in much the same way that you do using integers.

Example

$$-2\frac{3}{8} \times 6\frac{4}{9} = -\frac{19}{8} \times \frac{58}{9}$$

$$= -\frac{1102}{72}$$

$$= -15\frac{22}{72}$$

$$= -15\frac{11}{36}$$

5.2 Identifying Terminating and Repeating Decimals

A terminating decimal is a decimal that has a last digit. A repeating decimal is a decimal with digits that repeat in sets of one or more. Two different notations are used to represent repeating decimals. One notation is to write the decimal, including one set of digits that repeat, and place a bar over the repeating digits. Another notation is to write the decimal, including two sets of the digits that repeat, and using dots to indicate repetition.

Examples

$\frac{7}{8}$ is a terminating decimal: and $\frac{4}{9}$ is a repeating decimal:

$$\frac{7}{8} = 8\overline{)7.000}^{\,0.875} \qquad\qquad \frac{4}{9} = 9\overline{)4.000}^{\,0.444}$$

$$\frac{7}{8} = 0.875 \qquad\qquad\qquad \frac{4}{9} = 0.\overline{4}$$

5.2 Writing Repeating Decimals as Fractions

Some repeating decimals represent common fractions, such as $0.33... = \frac{1}{3}$, and are used often enough that we recognize the fraction by its decimal representation. However, there are decimals in which it is difficult to determine the fractional equivalent. To determine the fraction for the decimal, first, write an equation by setting the decimal equal to a variable that will represent the fraction. Next, write another equation by multiplying each side of the equation by a power of 10. The exponent on the power of 10 is equal to the number of decimal places until the decimal begins to repeat. Then, subtract the first equation from the second equation. Finally, solve the equation.

Example

The repeating decimal $0.\overline{15}$ is equal to the fraction $\frac{5}{33}$.

$$100w = 15.\overline{15}$$
$$\underline{-w = \;\;0.\overline{15}}$$
$$99w = 15$$
$$w = \frac{15}{99}$$
$$w = \frac{5}{33}$$

5.2 Identifying Irrational Numbers

Decimals that do not repeat and do not terminate are said to be irrational numbers. An irrational number is a number that cannot be written in the form $\frac{a}{b}$, where a and b are both integers and $b \neq 0$.

Example

An example of an irrational number is $\sqrt{11}$ because it is a square root that is not a perfect square and therefore has no repeating patterns of digits.

5.3 Classifying Numbers in the Real Number System

Combining the set of rational numbers and the set of irrational numbers produces the set of real numbers. Within the set of rational numbers, a number can be or not be an integer, whole number, natural number, or some combination.

Examples

π is an irrational number.

-8 is a rational number and an integer.

23 is a natural number, whole number, integer, and rational number.

$\frac{1}{4}$ is a rational number.

5.3 Understanding the Properties of Real Numbers

The real numbers, together with their operations and properties, form the real number system. The properties of real numbers include:

Closure: A set of numbers is said to be closed under an operation if the result of the operation on two numbers in the set is another member of the set.

Additive Identity: An additive identity is a number such that when you add it to a second number, the sum is equal to the second number.

Multiplicative Identity: A multiplicative identity is a number such that when you multiply it by a second number, the product is equal to the second number.

Additive Inverse: Two numbers are additive inverses if their sum is the additive identity.

Multiplicative Inverse: Two numbers are multiplicative inverses if their product is the multiplicative identity.

Commutative Property of Addition: Changing the order of two or more addends in an addition problem does not change the sum.

Commutative Property of Multiplication: Changing the order of two or more factors in a multiplication problem does not change the product.

Associative Property of Addition: Changing the grouping of the addends in an addition problem does not change the sum.

Associative Property of Multiplication: Changing the grouping of the factors in a multiplication problem does not change the product.

Reflexive Property of Equality: For any real number a, $a = a$.

Symmetric Property of Equality: For any real numbers a and b, if $a = b$, then $b = a$.

Transitive Property of Equality: For any real numbers a, b, and c, if $a = b$ and $b = c$, then $a = c$.

Examples

$128 + (-128) = 0$ shows the additive inverse.

$13 \times (-7) = -7 \times 13$ shows the commutative property of multiplication.

$89 \times 1 = 89$ shows the multiplicative identity.

$(31 \times x) + y = 31 + (x + y)$ shows the associative property of addition.

If $x = 7 + y$ and $7 + y = 21$, then $x = 21$ shows the transitive property of equality.

Hopefully you didn't become irrational during this chapter! Remember keep a positive attitude—it makes a difference!

5

5

PYTHAGOREAN THEOREM

What is the distance from the Earth to the Moon? Don't let drawings or even photos fool you. A lot of them can be misleading, making the Moon appear closer than it really is, which is about 250,000 miles away.

6

6.1

SOON YOU WILL DETERMINE THE RIGHT TRIANGLE CONNECTION

The Pythagorean Theorem

Learning Goals

In this lesson, you will:

- ▶ Use mathematical properties to discover the Pythagorean Theorem.
- ▶ Solve problems involving right triangles.

Key Terms

- ▶ right triangle
- ▶ right angle
- ▶ leg
- ▶ hypotenuse
- ▶ diagonal of a square
- ▶ Pythagorean Theorem
- ▶ theorem
- ▶ postulate
- ▶ proof

What do firefighters and roofers have in common? If you said they both use ladders, you would be correct! Many people who use ladders as part of their job must also take a class in ladder safety. What type of safety tips would you recommend? Do you think the angle of the ladder is important to safety?

Problem 1   Identifying the Sides of Right Triangles

A **right triangle** is a triangle with a right angle. A **right angle** has a measure of 90° and is indicated by a square drawn at the corner formed by the angle. A **leg** of a right triangle is either of the two shorter sides. Together, the two legs form the right angle of a right triangle. The **hypotenuse** of a right triangle is the longest side. The hypotenuse is opposite the right angle.

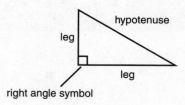

right angle symbol

1. The side lengths of right triangles are given. Determine which length represents the hypotenuse.

   a. 5, 12, 13

   b. 1, 1, $\sqrt{2}$

   c. 2.4, 5.1, 4.5

   d. 75, 21, 72

   e. 15, 39, 36

   f. 7, 24, 25

2. How did you decide which length represented the hypotenuse?

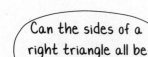

Can the sides of a right triangle all be the same length?

Problem 2   Exploring Right Triangles

In this problem, you will explore three different right triangles. You will draw squares on each side of the triangles and then answer questions about the completed figures.

A **diagonal of a square** is a line segment connecting opposite vertices of the square. Let's explore the side lengths of more right triangles.

1. An isosceles right triangle is drawn on the grid shown on page 317.

   a. A square on the hypotenuse has been drawn for you. Use a straightedge to draw squares on the other two sides of the triangle. Then use different colored pencils to shade each small square.

   b. Draw two diagonals in each of the two smaller squares.

   c. Cut out the two smaller squares along the legs. Then, cut those squares into fourths along the diagonals you drew.

   d. Redraw the squares on the figure in the graphic organizer on page 327. Shade the smaller squares again.

   e. Arrange the pieces you cut out to fit inside the larger square on the graphic organizer. Then, tape the triangles on top of the larger square.

Answer these questions in the graphic organizer.

   f. What do you notice?

   g. Write a sentence that describes the relationship among the areas of the squares.

   h. Determine the length of the hypotenuse of the right triangle. Justify your solution.

Remember,
$A = s^2$ so,
$\sqrt{A} = s$.

Remember that you can estimate the value of a square root by using the square roots of perfect squares.

$$\sqrt{1} \quad \sqrt{4} \quad \sqrt{9} \quad \sqrt{16} \quad \sqrt{25} \quad \sqrt{36} \quad \sqrt{49} \quad \sqrt{64} \quad \sqrt{81}$$

1   2   3   4   5   6   7   8   9

$\sqrt{40}$

The square root of 40 is between $\sqrt{36}$ and $\sqrt{49}$, or between 6 and 7. $\sqrt{40} \approx 6.3$.

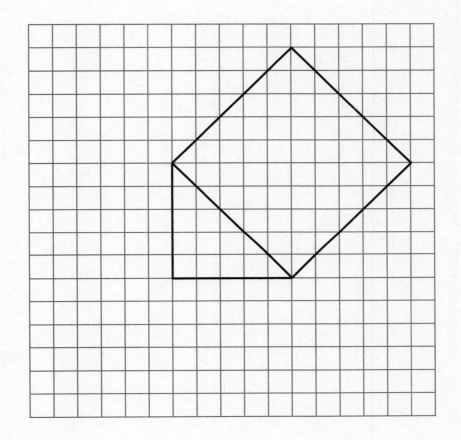

2. A right triangle is shown on page 321 with one leg 4 units in length and the other leg 3 units in length.

   a. Use a straightedge to draw squares on each side of the triangle. Use different colored pencils to shade each square along the legs.

   b. Cut out the two smaller squares along the legs.

   c. Cut the two squares into strips that are either 4 units by 1 unit or 3 units by 1 unit.

   d. Redraw the squares on the figure in the graphic organizer on page 328. Shade the smaller squares again.

   e. Arrange the strips and squares you cut out on top of the square along the hypotenuse on the graphic organizer. You may need to make additional cuts to the strips to create individual squares that are 1 unit by 1 unit. Then, tape the strips on top of the square you drew on the hypotenuse.

Answer these questions in the graphic organizer.

   f. What do you notice?

   g. Write a sentence that describes the relationship among the areas of the squares.

   h. Determine the length of the hypotenuse. Justify your solution.

Remember, the length of the side of a square is the square root of its area.

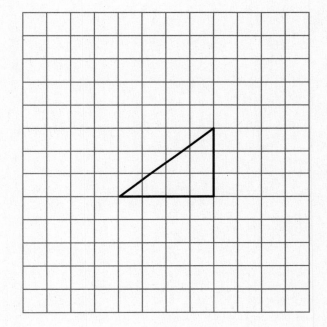

6

3. A right triangle is shown on page 325 with one leg 2 units in length and the other leg 4 units in length.

   a. Use a straightedge to draw squares on each side of the triangle. Use different colored pencils to shade each square along the legs.

   b. Cut out the two smaller squares.

   c. Draw four congruent right triangles on the square with side lengths of 4 units. Then, cut out the four congruent right triangles you drew.

   d. Redraw the squares on the figure in the graphic organizer on page 329. Shade the smaller squares again.

   e. Arrange and tape the small square and the 4 congruent triangles you cut out over the square that has one of its sides as the hypotenuse.

Answer these questions in the graphic organizer.

   f. What do you notice?

   g. Write a sentence that describes the relationship among the areas of the squares.

   h. Determine the length of the hypotenuse. Justify your solution.

4. Compare the sentences you wrote for part (f) in Questions 1, 2, and 3. What do you notice?

5. Write an equation that represents the relationship among the areas of the squares. Assume that the length of one leg of the right triangle is "*a*," the length of the other leg of the right triangle is "*b*," and the length of the hypotenuse is "*c*."

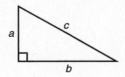

6

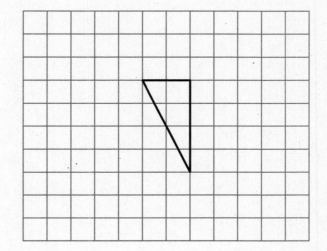

WHAT DO YOU NOTICE?

DESCRIBE THE RELATIONSHIP AMONG THE AREAS OF THE SQUARES.

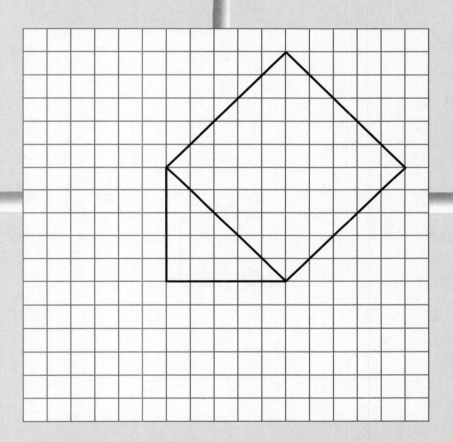

DETERMINE THE LENGTH OF THE HYPOTENUSE.

WHAT DO YOU NOTICE?

DESCRIBE THE RELATIONSHIP AMONG THE AREAS OF THE SQUARES.

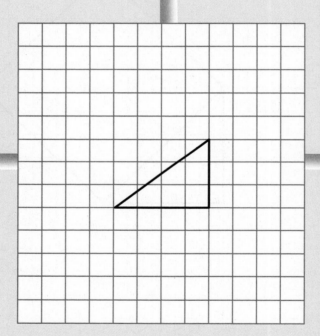

DETERMINE THE LENGTH OF THE HYPOTENUSE

RIGHT TRIANGLE: ONE LEG WITH LENGTH OF 2 UNITS
AND THE OTHER LEG WITH LENGTH OF 4 UNITS

WHAT DO YOU NOTICE?

DESCRIBE THE RELATIONSHIP AMONG THE AREAS OF THE SQUARES.

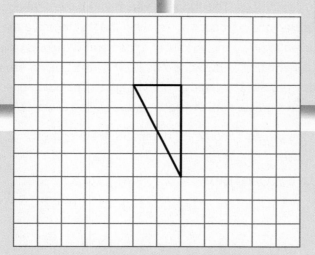

DETERMINE THE LENGTH OF THE HYPOTENUSE.

Problem 3   Special Relationships

The special relationship that exists between the squares of the lengths of the sides of a right triangle is known as the *Pythagorean Theorem*. The sum of the squares of the lengths of the legs of a right triangle equals the square of the length of the hypotenuse.

The **Pythagorean Theorem** states that if a and b are the lengths of the legs of a right triangle and c is the length of the hypotenuse, then $a^2 + b^2 = c^2$.

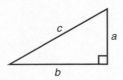

A **theorem** is a mathematical statement that can be proven using definitions, *postulates*, and other theorems. A **postulate** is a mathematical statement that cannot be proved but is considered true. The Pythagorean Theorem is one of the earliest known to ancient civilization and one of the most famous. This theorem was named after Pythagoras (580 to 496 B.C.), a Greek mathematician and philosopher who was the first to *prove* the theorem. A **proof** is a series of steps used to prove the validity of a theorem. While it is called the Pythagorean Theorem, the mathematical knowledge was used by the Babylonians 1000 years before Pythagoras. Many proofs followed that of Pythagoras, including ones proved by Euclid, Socrates, and even the twentieth President of the United States, President James A. Garfield.

1. Use the Pythagorean Theorem to determine the length of the hypotenuse:

    a. in Problem 2, Question 1.

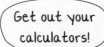

Get out your calculators!

    b. in Problem 2, Question 3.

6

Problem 4   Maintaining School Grounds

Mitch maintains the Magnolia Middle School campus. Use the Pythagorean Theorem to help Mitch with some of his jobs.

1. Mitch needs to wash the windows on the second floor of a building. He knows the windows are 12 feet above the ground. Because of dense shrubbery, he has to put the base of the ladder 5 feet from the building. What ladder length does he need?

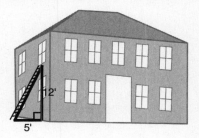

2. The gym teacher, Ms. Fisher, asked Mitch to put up the badminton net. Ms. Fisher said that the top of the net must be 5 feet above the ground. She knows that Mitch will need to put stakes in the ground for rope supports. She asked that the stakes be placed 6 feet from the base of the poles. Mitch has two pieces of rope, one that is 7 feet long and a second that is 8 feet long. Will these two pieces of rope be enough to secure the badminton poles? Explain your reasoning.

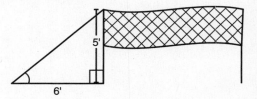

3. Mitch stopped by the baseball field to watch the team practice. The first baseman caught a line drive right on the base. He touched first base for one out and quickly threw the ball to third base to get another out. How far did he throw the ball?

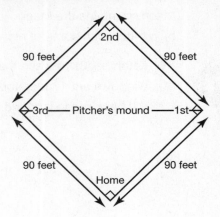

4. The skate ramp on the playground of a neighboring park is going to be replaced. Mitch needs to determine how long the ramp is to get estimates on the cost of a new skate ramp. He knows the measurements shown in the figure. How long is the existing skate ramp?

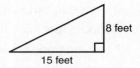

5. A wheelchair ramp that is constructed to rise 1 foot off the ground must extend 12 feet along the ground. How long will the wheelchair ramp be?

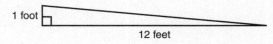

6. The eighth-grade math class keeps a flower garden in the front of the building. The garden is in the shape of a right triangle, and its dimensions are shown. The class wants to install a 3-foot-high picket fence around the garden to keep students from stepping onto the flowers. The picket fence they need costs $5 a linear foot. How much will the fence cost? Do not calculate sales tax. Show your work and justify your solution.

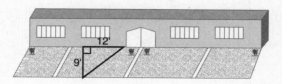

Problem 5 Solving for the Unknown Side

1. Write an equation to determine each unknown length. Then, solve the equation. Make sure your answer is simplified.

a.

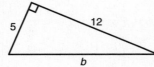

b.

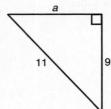

c.

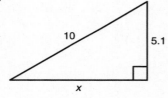

d.

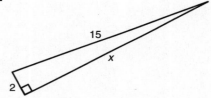

Be prepared to share your solutions and methods.

6.2 CAN THAT BE RIGHT?

The Converse of the Pythagorean Theorem

Learning Goal

In this lesson, you will:

▶ Use the Pythagorean Theorem and the Converse of the Pythagorean Theorem to determine unknown side lengths in right triangles.

Key Terms

▶ converse
▶ Converse of the Pythagorean Theorem
▶ Pythagorean triple

"**M**ind your *p*'s and *q*'s!" This statement usually refers to reminding a person to watch their manners. While the definition is easy to understand, the origin of this saying is not clear. Some people think that it comes from a similar reminder for people to remember their "please and thank-yous" where the "*q*'s" rhymes with "yous." Others believe that it was a reminder to young children not to mix up *p*'s and *q*'s when writing because both letters look very similar.

However, maybe the origin of this saying comes from math. When working with theorems (as you did in the last lesson), mathematicians encounter if-then statements. Often, if-then statements are defined as "if *p*, then *q*," with the *p* representing an assumption and the *q* representing the outcome of the assumption. So, just maybe math played a role in this saying.

6

Problem 1 The Converse

The Pythagorean Theorem can be used to solve many problems involving right triangles, squares, and rectangles. The Pythagorean Theorem states that in a right triangle, the square of the hypotenuse length equals the sum of the squares of the leg lengths. In other words, if you have a right triangle with a hypotenuse of length c and legs of lengths a and b, then $a^2 + b^2 = c^2$.

The **converse** of a theorem is created when the if-then parts of that theorem are exchanged.

The **Converse of the Pythagorean Theorem** states that if $a^2 + b^2 = c^2$, then the triangle is a right triangle.

If the lengths of the sides of a triangle satisfy the equation $a^2 + b^2 = c^2$, then the triangle is a right triangle.

1. Determine whether the triangle with the given side lengths is a right triangle.

   a. 9, 12, 15

Think about which measures represent legs of the right triangle and which measure represents the hypotenuse.

   b. 24, 45, 51

   c. 25, 16, 9

   d. 8, 8, 11

You may have noticed that each of the right triangles in Question 1 had side lengths that were integers. Any set of three positive integers a, b, and c that satisfies the equation $a^2 + b^2 = c^2$ is a **Pythagorean triple**. For example, the integers 3, 4, and 5 form a Pythagorean triple because $3^2 + 4^2 = 5^2$.

2. Complete the table to identify more Pythagorean triples.

	a	b	c	Check: $a^2 + b^2 = c^2$
Pythagorean triple	3	4	5	$9 + 16 = 25$
Multiply by 2				
Multiply by 3				
Multiply by 5				

What if I multiplied 3, 4, and 5 each by a decimal like 2.2? Would those side lengths form a right triangle?

3. Determine a new Pythagorean triple not used in Question 2, and complete the table.

	a	b	c	Check: $a^2 + b^2 = c^2$
Pythagorean triple				
Multiply by 2				
Multiply by 3				
Multiply by 5				

6

4. Record other Pythagorean triples that your classmates determined.

Problem 2   Solving Problems

1. A carpenter attaches a brace to a rectangular-shaped picture frame. If the dimensions of the picture frame are 30 inches by 40 inches, what is the length of the brace?

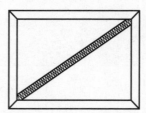

2. Bill is building a rectangular deck that will be 8 feet wide and 15 feet long. Tyrone is helping Bill with the deck. Tyrone has two boards, one that is 8 feet long and one that is 7 feet long. He puts the two boards together, end to end, and lays them on the diagonal of the deck area, where they just fit. What should he tell Bill?

3. A television is identified by the diagonal measurement of the screen. A television has a 36-inch screen whose height is 22 inches. What is the length of the television screen? Round your answer to the nearest inch.

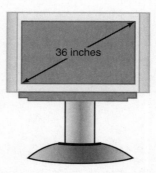

36 inches

4. Orville and Jerri want to put a custom-made, round table in their dining room. The table top is made of glass with a diameter of 85 inches. The front door is 36 inches wide and 80 inches tall. Orville thinks the table top will fit through the door, but Jerri does not. Who is correct and why?

5. Sherie makes a canvas frame for a painting using stretcher bars. The rectangular painting will be 12 inches long and 9 inches wide. How can she use a ruler to make sure that the corners of the frame will be right angles?

6. A 10-foot ladder is placed 4 feet from the edge of a building. How far up the building does the ladder reach? Round your answer to the nearest tenth of a foot.

6

7. Chris has a tent that is 64 inches wide with a slant length of 68 inches on each side. What is the height of the center pole needed to prop up the tent?

8. A ship left shore and sailed 240 kilometers east, turned due north, then sailed another 70 kilometers. How many kilometers is the ship from shore by the most direct path?

9. Tonya walks to school every day. She must travel 4 blocks east and 3 blocks south around a parking lot. Upon arriving at school, she realizes that she forgot her math homework. In a panic, she decides to run back home to get her homework by taking a shortcut through the parking lot.

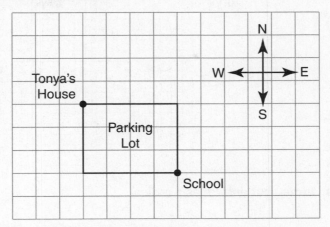

a. Describe how many blocks long Tonya's shortcut is.

b. How many fewer blocks did Tonya walk by taking the shortcut?

10. Danielle walks 88 feet due east to the library from her house. From the library, she walks 187 feet northwest to the corner store. Finally, she walks 57 feet from the corner store back home. Does she live directly south of the corner store? Justify your answer.

11. What is the diagonal length of a square that has a side length of 10 cm?

12. Calculate the length of the segment that connects the points (1, −5) and (3, 6).

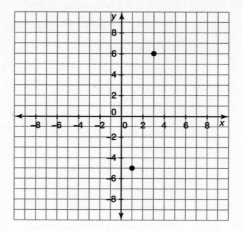

    a. Write your answer as a radical.

    b. Write your answer as a decimal rounded to the nearest hundredth.

 Be prepared to share your solutions and methods.

6.3 PYTHAGORAS TO THE RESCUE

Solving for Unknown Lengths

Learning Goal

In this lesson, you will:

▶ Use the Pythagorean Theorem and the Converse of the Pythagorean Theorem to determine the unknown side lengths in right triangles.

There's a very famous mathematical scene in the movie *The Wizard of Oz*. At the end, when the wizard helps the scarecrow realize that he has had a brain all along, the scarecrow says this:

"The sum of the square roots of any two sides of an isosceles triangle is equal to the square root of the remaining side. Oh joy! Rapture! I've got a brain! How can I ever thank you enough?"

What did the scarecrow get wrong?

Problem 1   Determining the Length of the Hypotenuse

In this lesson, you will investigate solving for different side lengths of right triangles and using the converse of the Pythagorean Theorem.

Determine the length of the hypotenuse of each triangle. Round your answer to the nearest tenth, if necessary.

1.

2.

3.

4.

Problem 2   Determining the Length of a Leg

Determine the unknown leg length. Round your answer to the nearest tenth, if necessary.

1.

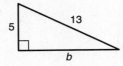

5   13   b

2.

a   15   12

3.

a   10   5

4.

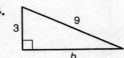

3   9   b

Problem 3   Determining the Right Triangle

Use the converse of the Pythagorean Theorem to determine whether each triangle is a right triangle. Explain your answer.

1.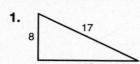

2.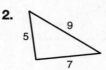

3.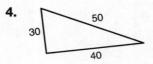

4.

Problem 4 Determining the Unknown Length

Use the Pythagorean Theorem to calculate each unknown length. Round your answer to the nearest tenth, if necessary.

1. Chandra has a ladder that is 20 feet long. If the top of the ladder reaches 16 feet up the side of a building, how far from the building is the base of the ladder?

2. A scaffold has a diagonal support beam to strengthen it. If the scaffold is 12 feet high and 5 feet wide, how long must the support beam be?

3. The length of the hypotenuse of a right triangle is 40 centimeters. The legs of the triangle are the same length. How long is each leg of the triangle?

4. A carpenter props a ladder against the wall of a building. The base of the ladder is 10 feet from the wall. The top of the ladder is 24 feet from the ground. How long is the ladder?

> The Pythagorean Theorem is very useful. You just have to pay attention to what the problem is asking.

Be prepared to share your solutions and methods.

MEETING FRIENDS

The Distance Between Two Points in a Coordinate System

6.4

Learning Goal

In this lesson, you will:

▶ Use the Pythagorean Theorem to determine the distance between two points in a coordinate system.

Try this in your class. All you need is a regulation size basketball (29.5 inches in diameter), a tennis ball, and a tape measure. Have your teacher hold the basketball, and give the tennis ball to a student. The basketball represents the Earth, and the tennis ball represents the Moon.

Here's the question each student should guess at: How far away from the basketball should you hold the tennis ball so that the distance between the two represents the actual distance between the Earth and the Moon to scale?

Use the tape measure to record each student's guess. Have your teacher show you the answer when you're done. See who can get the closest.

Problem 1   Meeting at the Bookstore

Two friends, Shawn and Tamara, live in a city in which the streets are laid out in a grid system.

Shawn lives on Descartes Avenue and Tamara lives on Elm Street as shown. The two friends often meet at the bookstore. Each grid square represents one city block.

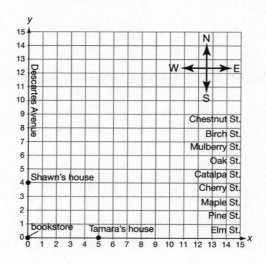

1. How many blocks does Shawn walk to get to the bookstore?

2. How many blocks does Tamara walk to get to the bookstore?

3. Determine the distance, in blocks, Tamara would walk if she traveled from her house to the bookstore and then to Shawn's house.

4. Determine the distance, in blocks, Tamara would walk if she traveled in a straight line from her house to Shawn's house. Explain your calculation. Round your answer to the nearest tenth of a block.

5. Don, a friend of Shawn and Tamara, lives three blocks east of Descartes Avenue and five blocks north of Elm Street. Freda, another friend, lives seven blocks east of Descartes Avenue and two blocks north of Elm Street. Plot the location of Don's house and Freda's house on the grid. Label each location and label the coordinates of each location.

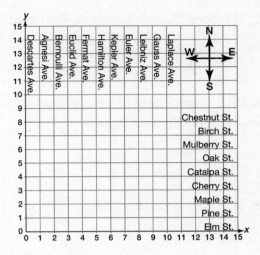

   a. Name the streets that Don lives on.

   b. Name the streets that Freda lives on.

6. Another friend, Bert, lives at the intersection of the avenue that Don lives on and the street that Freda lives on. Plot the location of Bert's house on the grid in Question 5 and label the coordinates. Describe the location of Bert's house with respect to Descartes Avenue and Elm Street.

7. How do the coordinates of Bert's house compare to the coordinates of Don's house and Freda's house?

8. Use the house coordinates to write and evaluate an expression that represents the distance between Don's and Bert's houses.

9. How far, in blocks, does Don have to walk to get to Bert's house?

10. Use the house coordinates to write an expression that represents the distance between Bert's and Freda's houses.

11. How far, in blocks, does Bert have to walk to get to Freda's house?

12. All three friends meet at Don's house to study geometry. Freda walks to Bert's house, and then they walk together to Don's house. Use the coordinates to write and evaluate an expression that represents the distance from Freda's house to Bert's house and from Bert's house to Don's house.

13. How far, in blocks, does Freda walk altogether?

14. Draw the direct path from Don's house to Freda's house on the coordinate plane in Question 5. If Freda walks to Don's house on this path, how far, in blocks, does she walk? Explain how you determined your answer.

6

Problem 2　The Distance between Two Points

1. The points (1, 2) and (3, 7) on are shown on the coordinate plane. You can calculate the distance between these two points by drawing a right triangle. When you think about this line segment as the hypotenuse of the right triangle, you can use the Pythagorean Theorem.

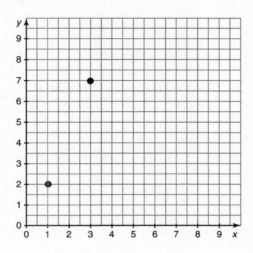

a. Connect the points with a line segment. Draw a right triangle with this line segment as the hypotenuse.

b. What are the lengths of each leg of the right triangle?

c. Use the Pythagorean Theorem to determine the length of the hypotenuse. Round your answer to the nearest tenth.

So, if you think of the distance between two points as a hypotenuse, you can draw a right triangle and then use the Pythagorean Theorem to find its length.

6

Determine the distance between each pair of points by graphing and connecting the points, creating a right triangle, and applying the Pythagorean Theorem.

2. (3, 4) and (6, 8)

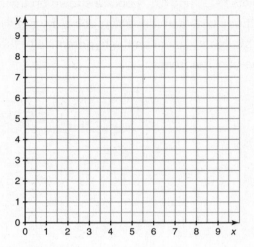

Make sure to pay attention to the intervals shown on the axes.

3. (−6, 4) and (2, −8)

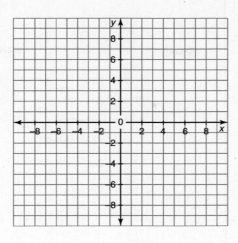

4. (−5, 2) and (−6, 10)

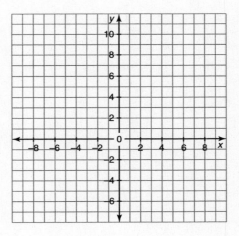

5. $(-1, -4)$ and $(-3, -6)$

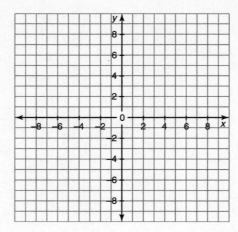

Be prepared to share your solutions and methods.

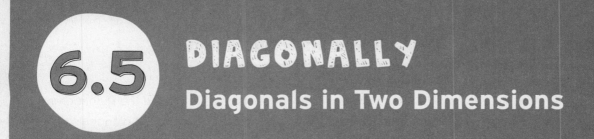

6.5 DIAGONALLY
Diagonals in Two Dimensions

Learning Goal

In this lesson, you will:

▶ Use the Pythagorean Theorem to determine the length of diagonals in two-dimensional figures.

You have certainly seen signs like this one.

This sign means "no parking." In fact, a circle with a diagonal line through it (from top left to bottom right) is considered the universal symbol for "no." This symbol is used on street signs, on packaging, and on clothing labels, to name just a few.

What other examples can you name?

Problem 1   Diagonals of a Rectangle and a Square

Previously, you have drawn or created many right triangles and used the Pythagorean Theorem to determine side lengths. In this lesson, you will explore the diagonals of various shapes.

1. Rectangle *ABCD* is shown.

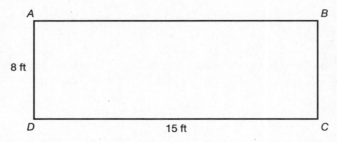

a. Draw diagonal *AC* in rectangle *ABCD*. Then, determine the length of diagonal *AC*.

Be on the look out for right triangles.

b. Draw diagonal *BD* in rectangle *ABCD*. Then, determine the length of diagonal *BD*.

c. What can you conclude about the diagonals of this rectangle?

2. Square *ABCD* is shown.

A ⌐――――――――――⌐ B

10 m

D ⌐――――――――――⌐ C

a. Draw diagonal *AC* in square *ABCD*. Then, determine the length of diagonal *AC*.

b. Draw diagonal *BD* in square *ABCD*. Then, determine the length of diagonal *BD*.

c. What can you conclude about the diagonals of this square?

All squares are also rectangles, does your conclusion make sense.

6

Problem 2   Diagonals of Trapezoids

1. Graph and label the coordinates of the vertices of trapezoid *ABCD*.
   A(1, 2), *B*(7, 2), *C*(7, 5), *D*(3, 5)

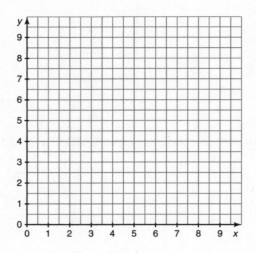

   a. Draw diagonal *AC* in trapezoid *ABCD*.

   b. What right triangle can be used to determine the length of diagonal *AC*?

   c. Determine the length of diagonal *AC*.

   > By examining the two right triangles, what prediction can you make about the diagonals of this trapezoid?

6

   d. Draw diagonal *BD* in trapezoid *ABCD*.

   e. What right triangle can be used to determine the length of diagonal *BD*?

f. Determine the length of diagonal *BD*.

g. What can you conclude about the diagonals of this trapezoid?

2. Graph and label the coordinates of the vertices of isosceles trapezoid *ABCD*.
A(1, 2), *B*(9, 2), *C*(7, 5), *D*(3, 5)

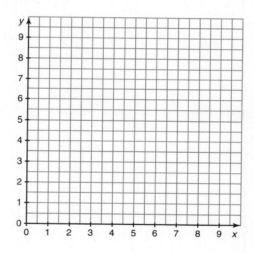

How is this trapezoid different than the first trapezoid you drew?

a. Draw diagonal *AC* in trapezoid *ABCD*.

b. What right triangle can be used to determine the length of diagonal *AC*?

c. Determine the length of diagonal *AC*.

d. Draw diagonal *BD* in trapezoid *ABCD*.

e. What right triangle can be used to determine the length of diagonal *BD*?

f. Determine the length of diagonal *BD*.

What is your prediction about the diagonals of this isosceles triangle?

g. What can you conclude about the diagonals of this isosceles trapezoid?

Problem 3   Composite Figures

Use your knowledge of right triangles, the Pythagorean Theorem, and areas of shapes to determine the area of each shaded region. Use 3.14 for π.

1. A rectangle is inscribed in a circle as shown.

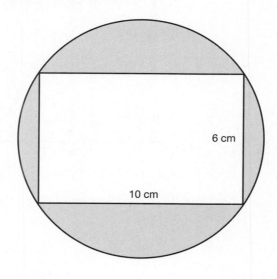

6 cm

10 cm

Think about how the diagonal of the rectangle relates to the diameter of the circle.

2. The figure is composed of a right triangle and a semi-circle.

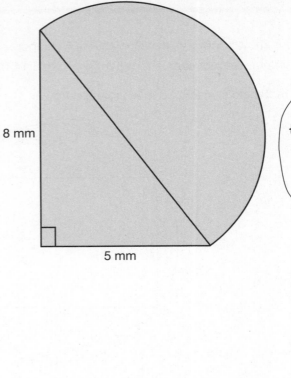

8 mm

5 mm

Think about how the hypotenuse of the right triangle relates to the semi-circle.

Be prepared to share your solutions and methods.

6.6 TWO DIMENSIONS MEET THREE DIMENSIONS

Diagonals in Three Dimensions

Learning Goals

In this lesson, you will:

▶ Use the Pythagorean Theorem to determine the length of a diagonal of a solid.

▶ Use a formula to determine the length of a diagonal of a rectangular solid given the lengths of three perpendicular edges.

▶ Use a formula to determine the length of a diagonal of a rectangular solid given the diagonal measurements of three perpendicular sides.

Harry Houdini was one of the most famous escapologists in history. What is an escapologist? He or she is a person who is an expert at escaping from restraints—like handcuffs, cages, barrels, fish tanks, and boxes.

On July 7, 1912, Houdini performed an amazing box escape. He was handcuffed, and his legs were shackled together. He was then placed in a box which was nailed shut, roped, weighed down with 200 pounds of lead, and then lowered into the East River in New York!

Houdini managed to escape in less than a minute. But he was a professional. So don't try to become an escapologist at home!

6

Problem 1 A Box of Roses

A rectangular box of long-stem roses is 18 inches in length, 6 inches in width, and 4 inches in height.

Without bending a long-stem rose, you are to determine the maximum length of a rose that will fit into the box.

How can the Pythagorean Theorem help you solve this problem?

1. What makes this problem different from all of the previous applications of the Pythagorean Theorem?

2. Compare a two-dimensional diagonal to a three-dimensional diagonal. Describe the similarities and differences.

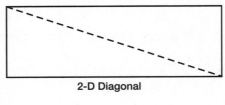

2-D Diagonal

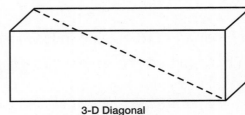

3-D Diagonal

3. Which diagonal represents the maximum length of a rose that can fit into a box?

4. Draw all of the sides in the rectangular solid you cannot see using dotted lines.

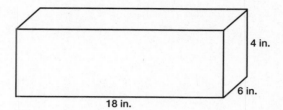

4 in.

6 in.

18 in.

5. Draw a three-dimensional diagonal in the rectangular solid shown.

6. Let's consider that the three-dimensional diagonal you drew in the rectangular solid is also the hypotenuse of a right triangle. If a vertical edge is one of the legs of that right triangle, where is the second leg of that same right triangle?

7. Draw the second leg using a dotted line. Then lightly shade the right triangle.

8. Determine the length of the second leg you drew.

9. Determine the length of the three-dimensional diagonal.

Does how you choose to round numbers in your calculations affect your final answer?

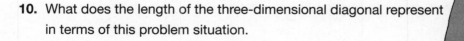

10. What does the length of the three-dimensional diagonal represent in terms of this problem situation.

11. Describe how the Pythagorean Theorem was used to solve this problem.

Problem 2 Drawing Diagonals

Draw all of the sides you cannot see in each rectangular solid using dotted lines. Then draw a three-dimensional diagonal using a solid line.

1.

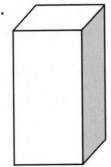

2.

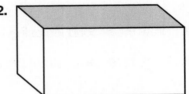

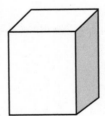

How many three-dimensional diagonals can be drawn in each figure?

3.

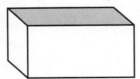

4.

5.

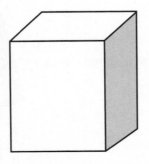

6.

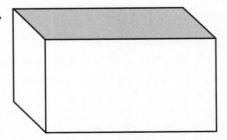

Problem 3 Applying the Pythagorean Theorem

Determine the length of the diagonal of each rectangular solid.

1.

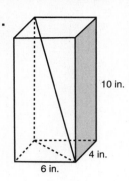

10 in.

4 in.

6 in.

2.

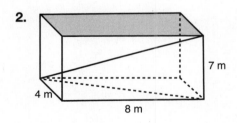

7 m

4 m

8 m

3.

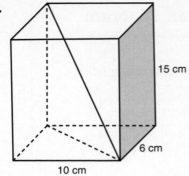

15 cm

6 cm

10 cm

4.

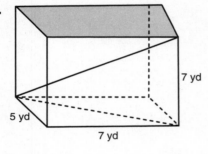

7 yd

5 yd

7 yd

5.

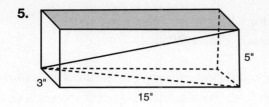

3" 15" 5"

6.

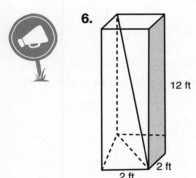

12 ft

2 ft 2 ft

Problem 4 Student Discovery

1. Norton thought he knew a shortcut for determining the length of a three-dimensional diagonal. He said, "All you have to do is calculate the sum of the squares of the rectangular solids' 3 perpendicular edges (the length, the width, and the height) and that sum would be equivalent to the square of the three-dimensional diagonal." Does this work? Use the rectangular solid in Problem 1 to determine if Norton is correct. Explain your reasoning.

2. Use Norton's strategy to calculate the length of the diagonals of each rectangular solid in Problem 3. How do these answers compare to the answers in Problem 3?

The square of a three-dimensional diagonal is equal to the sum of the squares of each dimension of the rectangular solid.

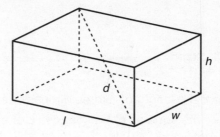

$$d^2 = \ell^2 + w^2 + h^2$$

$$d = \sqrt{\ell^2 + w^2 + h^2}$$

3. Use the formula $d = \sqrt{\ell^2 + w^2 + h^2}$ to determine the length of a three-dimensional diagonal of the rectangular prism shown.

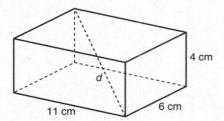

11 cm

6 cm

4 cm

If you know the diagonal lengths of each face of a rectangular solid, you can determine the length of a three-dimensional diagonal.

Let d represent the length of a three dimensional diagonal.
$d^2 = \frac{1}{2}$ (sum of the squares of the diagonals of each unique face)

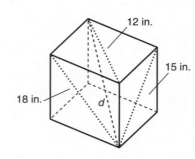
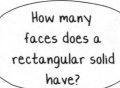

12 in.

15 in.

18 in.

d

How many faces does a rectangular solid have?

$d^2 = \frac{1}{2}(18^2 + 15^2 + 12^2)$

$d^2 = \frac{1}{2}(324 + 225 + 144)$

$d^2 = 346.5$

$d = \sqrt{346.5}$

$d \approx 18.6$

The length of the three-dimensional diagonal of this rectangular prism is about 18.6 inches.

Use your knowledge of diagonals and the two formulas given to answer each question.

4. A rectangular box has a length of 6 feet and a width of 2 feet. The length of a three-dimensional diagonal of the box is 7 feet. What is the height of the box?

5. The length of the diagonal across the front of a rectangular box is 20 inches, and the length of the diagonal across the side of the box is 15 inches. The length of a three-dimensional diagonal of the box is 23 inches. What is the length of the diagonal across the top of the box?

6. Pablo is packing for a business trip. He is almost finished packing when he realizes that he forgot to pack his umbrella. Before Pablo takes the time to repack his suitcase, he wants to know if the umbrella will fit in the suitcase. His suitcase is in the shape of a rectangular prism and has a length of 2 feet, a width of 1.5 feet, and a height of 0.75 foot. The umbrella is 30 inches long. Will the umbrella fit in Pablo's suitcase? Explain your reasoning.

 Be prepared to share your solutions and methods.

6

Chapter 6   Summary

Key Terms

- right triangle (6.1)
- right angle (6.1)
- leg (6.1)
- hypotenuse (6.1)
- diagonal of a square (6.1)

- Pythagorean Theorem (6.1)
- theorem (6.1)
- postulate (6.1)
- proof (6.1)

- converse (6.2)
- Converse of the Pythagorean Theorem (6.2)
- Pythagorean triple (6.2)

6.1   Applying the Pythagorean Theorem

A right triangle is a triangle with a right angle. A right angle is an angle with a measure of 90° and is indicated by a square drawn at the corner formed by the angle. A leg of a right triangle is either of the two shorter sides. Together, the two legs form the right angle of a right triangle. The hypotenuse of a right triangle is the longest side and is opposite the right angle. The Pythagorean Theorem states that if a and b are the lengths of the legs of a right triangle and c is the length of the hypotenuse, then $a^2 + b^2 = c^2$.

Example

Determine the unknown side length of the triangle.

$$a^2 + b^2 = c^2$$
$$4^2 + 8^2 = c^2$$
$$16 + 64 = c^2$$
$$80 = c^2$$
$$\sqrt{80} = c$$
$$c \approx 8.9$$

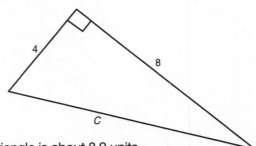

The unknown side length of the triangle is about 8.9 units.

Whoo! My brain got a workout with that chapter. I better get a good night's sleep to recover from all that hard work!

6.2 Applying the Converse of the Pythagorean Theorem

The Converse of the Pythagorean Theorem states that if a, b, and c are the side lengths of a triangle and $a^2 + b^2 = c^2$, then the triangle is a right triangle.

Example

Determine whether a triangle with side lengths 5, 9, and 10 is a right triangle.

$$a^2 + b^2 = c^2$$
$$5^2 + 9^2 \stackrel{?}{=} 10^2$$
$$25 + 81 \stackrel{?}{=} 100$$
$$106 \neq 100$$

A triangle with side lengths 5, 9, and 10 is not a right triangle because $5^2 + 9^2 \neq 10^2$.

6.3 Applying the Pythagorean Theorem to Solve Real-World Problems

The Pythagorean Theorem can be used to solve a variety of real-world problems which can be represented by right triangles.

Example

An escalator in a department store carries customers from the first floor to the second floor. Determine the distance between the two floors.

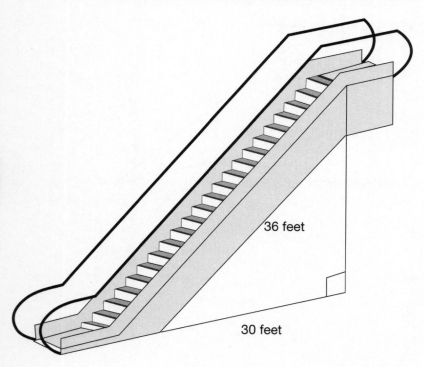

36 feet

30 feet

$$a^2 + b^2 = c^2$$
$$30^2 + b^2 = 36^2$$
$$900 + b^2 = 1296$$
$$b^2 = 396$$
$$b = \sqrt{396}$$
$$b \approx 19.90$$

The distance between the two floors is 19.90 feet.

6.4 Determining the Distance Between Two Points in a Coordinate System

The distance between two points, which do not lie on the same horizontal or vertical line, on a coordinate plane can be determined using the Pythagorean Theorem.

Example

Determine the distance between points $(-5, 3)$ and $(7, -2)$.

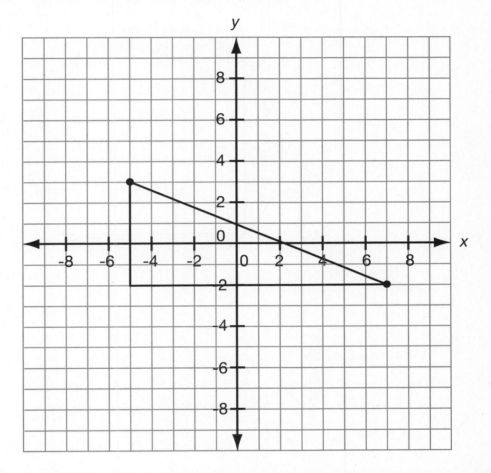

A line segment is drawn between the two points to represent the hypotenuse of a right triangle. Two line segments are drawn (one horizontal and one vertical) to represent the legs of the right triangle. The lengths of the legs are 5 units and 12 units.

$$a^2 + b^2 = c^2$$
$$5^2 + 12^2 = c^2$$
$$25 + 144 = c^2$$
$$c^2 = 169$$
$$c = \sqrt{169}$$
$$c = 13$$

The distance between $(-5, 3)$ and $(7, -2)$ is 13 units.

6.5 Determining the Lengths of Diagonals Using the Pythagorean Theorem

The Pythagorean Theorem can be a useful tool for determining the length of a diagonal in a two-dimensional figure.

Example

Determine the area of the shaded region.

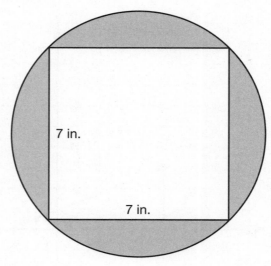

The area of the square is:

$A = s^2$
$A = 7^2$
$A = 49$ square inches

The diagonal of the square is the same length as the diameter of the circle. The diagonal of the square can be determined using the Pythagorean Theorem.

$a^2 + b^2 = c^2$
$7^2 + 7^2 = c^2$
$49 + 49 = c^2$
$c^2 = 98$
$c = \sqrt{98}$
$c \approx 9.90$ inches

So, the radius of the circle is $\frac{1}{2}(9.90) = 4.95$ inches
The area of the circle is:

$A = \pi r^2$
$A = (3.14)(4.95)^2$
$A \approx 76.94$ square inches

The area of the shaded region is $76.94 - 49 \approx 27.94$ square inches.

6.6 Determining the Lengths of Diagonals in Three-Dimensional Solids

The Pythagorean Theorem can be used to determine the length of a diagonal in a geometric solid. An alternate formula derived from the Pythagorean Theorem can also be used to determine the length of a diagonal in a geometric solid. In a right rectangular prism with length ℓ, width w, height h, and diagonal length d, $d^2 = \ell^2 + w^2 + h^2$.

Example

Determine the length of a diagonal in a right rectangular prism with a length of 4 feet, a width of 3 feet, and a height of 2 feet.

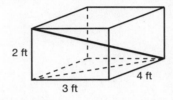

The diagonal is the hypotenuse of a triangle with one leg being the front left edge of the prism and the other leg being the diagonal of the bottom face.

The length of the diagonal of the bottom face is:

$a^2 + b^2 = c^2$

$3^2 + 4^2 = c^2$

$9 + 16 = c^2$

$\qquad c^2 = 25$

$\qquad c = \sqrt{25}$

$\qquad c = 5$ feet

The length of the prism's diagonal is:

$a^2 + b^2 = c^2$

$2^2 + 5^2 = c^2$

$4 + 25 = c^2$

$\qquad c^2 = 29$

$\qquad c = \sqrt{29}$

$\qquad c \approx 5.39$ feet

Using the alternate formula, the length of the prism's diagonal is:

$d^2 = \ell^2 + w^2 + h^2$

$d^2 = 4^2 + 3^2 + 2^2$

$d^2 = 16 + 9 + 4$

$d^2 = 29$

$d = \sqrt{29}$

$d \approx 5.39$ feet

7 TRANSLATIONS, REFLECTIONS, AND ROTATIONS

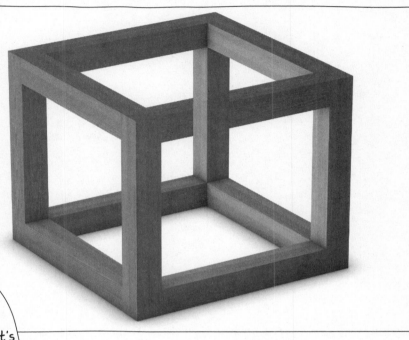

This photo shows a classic optical illusion called the Necker Cube. It's an example of an impossible object. Optical illusions are often helpful to scientists who study how we see the world around us. Can you see why this cube is "impossible"?

7

7

SLIDING RIGHT, LEFT, UP, DOWN, AND DIAGONALLY

Translations Using Geometric Figures

Learning Goals

In this lesson, you will:

▶ Translate geometric figures horizontally.

▶ Translate geometric figures vertically.

▶ Understand that a two-dimensional figure is congruent to another if the second can be obtained from the first by a sequence of translations.

Key Terms

▶ transformation

▶ translation

▶ image

▶ pre-image

To begin this chapter, cut out the figures shown on this page. You will have a trapezoid, two triangles, and a parallelogram. You will be using these figures in several lessons. What do you know about these shapes?

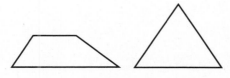

7

7

Problem 1 Sliding to the Right, Left, Up, and Down

Let's explore different ways to move, or transform, figures across a coordinate plane. A **transformation** is the mapping, or movement, of all the points of a figure in a plane according to a common operation.

1. Look at the parallelogram shown on the coordinate plane.

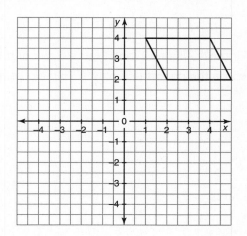

Make sure you check out the intervals used.

a. Place your parallelogram on the original figure on the coordinate plane shown and slide it 5 units to the left. Trace your parallelogram on the coordinate plane, and label it Figure 1.

b. Place your parallelogram on the original figure on the coordinate plane shown and slide it 5 units down. Trace your parallelogram on the coordinate plane, and label it Figure 2.

c. Place your parallelogram on Figure 1 on the coordinate plane and slide it 5 units down. Trace your parallelogram on the coordinate plane, and label it Figure 3.

Think about how the parallelograms are the same and different.

d. Describe how all of the parallelograms you traced on the coordinate plane compare with each other.

2. Recall that two geometric figures are considered congruent when they are the same size and the same shape.

    a. Did sliding the parallelogram either up or down on the coordinate plane change the size or shape of the parallelogram?

    b. Are Figure 1, Figure 2, and Figure 3 all congruent to the original parallelogram shown on the coordinate plane? Explain your reasoning.

When you were sliding the parallelogram to the different places, you were performing *translations* of the parallelogram. A **translation** is a transformation that "slides" each point of a figure the same distance and direction. Sliding a figure left or right is a horizontal translation, and sliding it up or down is a vertical translation. The new figure created from the translation is called the **image**. The original figure is called the **pre-image**.

3. Look at the triangle shown on the coordinate plane.

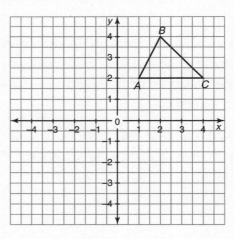

Again, check out the intervals.

    a. List the ordered pairs for the vertices of △*ABC*.

b. Place your triangle on △*ABC*, and translate it −6 units vertically. Trace the new triangle, and label the vertices *A'*, *B'*, and *C'* in △*A'B'C'* so the vertices correspond to the vertices *A*, *B*, and *C* in △*ABC*.

c. List the ordered pairs for the vertices of △*A'B'C'*.

d. Place your triangle on △*ABC*, and translate it −6 units horizontally. Trace the new triangle, and label the vertices *A"*, *B"*, and *C"* in △*A"B"C"* so the vertices correspond to the vertices *A*, *B*, and *C* in △*ABC*.

e. List the ordered pairs for the vertices of △*A"B"C"*.

f. Compare the ordered pairs in △*ABC* and △*A'B'C'*. How are the values in the ordered pairs affected by the translation?

g. Compare the ordered pairs in △*ABC* and △*A"B"C"*. How are the values in the ordered pairs affected by the translation?

h. If you were to translate △*ABC* 10 units vertically to form △*DEF*, what would be the ordered pairs of the corresponding vertices?

Which values of the ordered pair change by a horizontal move and which values change by a vertical move?

i. If you were to translate △*ABC* 10 units horizontally to form △*GHJ*, what would be the ordered pairs of the corresponding vertices?

7

4. Recall that two geometric figures are considered congruent when they are the same size and the same shape.

    a. Did sliding the triangle either up or down on the coordinate plane change the size or shape of the triangle?

    b. Are both of the triangles you drew congruent to the triangle shown on the coordinate plane? Explain your reasoning.

5. Look at the triangle shown on the coordinate plane.

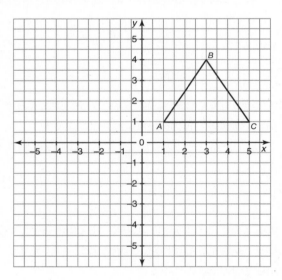

    a. List the ordered pairs for the vertices of $\triangle ABC$.

    b. Place your triangle on $\triangle ABC$, and translate it −5 units vertically. Trace the new triangle, and label the vertices A', B', and C' in $\triangle A'B'C'$ so the vertices correspond to the vertices A, B, and C in $\triangle ABC$.

    c. List the ordered pairs for the vertices of $\triangle A'B'C'$.

d. Place your triangle on △*ABC*, and translate it –5 units horizontally. Trace the new triangle, and label the vertices *A″*, *B″*, and *C″* in △*A″B″C″* so the vertices correspond to the vertices *A*, *B*, and *C* in △*ABC*.

e. List the ordered pairs for the vertices of △*A″B″C″*.

f. Compare the ordered pairs in △*ABC* and △*A′B′C′*. How are the values in the ordered pairs affected by the translation?

g. Compare the ordered pairs in △*ABC* and △*A″B″C″*. How are the values in the ordered pairs affected by the translation?

h. If you were to translate △*ABC* 10 units vertically to form △*DEF*, what would be the ordered pairs of the corresponding vertices?

Do you see any patterns?

i. If you were to translate △*ABC* 10 units horizontally to form △*GHJ*, what would be the ordered pairs of the corresponding vertices?

6. Are both triangles congruent to the original triangle shown on the coordinate plane? Explain your reasoning.

7

Problem 2   Translating a Trapezoid

1. Look at the trapezoid shown on the coordinate plane.

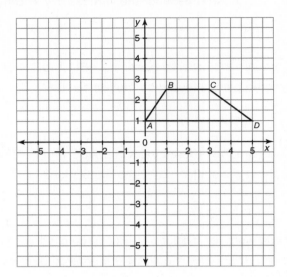

a. List the ordered pairs for the vertices of trapezoid *ABCD*.

b. Place your trapezoid on trapezoid *ABCD*, and translate it –5 units vertically. Trace the new trapezoid, and label the vertices *A'*, *B'*, *C'*, and *D'* in trapezoid *A'B'C'D'* so the vertices correspond to the vertices *A*, *B*, *C*, and *D* in trapezoid *ABCD*.

c. List the ordered pairs for the vertices of trapezoid *A'B'C'D'*.

d. Place your trapezoid on trapezoid *ABCD*, and translate it –5 units horizontally. Trace the new trapezoid, and label the vertices *A"*, *B"*, *C"*, and *D"* in trapezoid *A"B"C"D"* so the vertices correspond to the vertices *A*, *B*, *C*, and *D* in trapezoid *ABCD*.

e. List the ordered pairs for the vertices of trapezoid *A"B"C"D"*.

Can you predict what will happen to the ordered pairs of the trapezoid?

7

f. Compare the ordered pairs in trapezoid *ABCD* and trapezoid *A'B'C'D'*. How are the values in the ordered pairs affected by the translation?

g. Compare the ordered pairs in trapezoid *ABCD* and trapezoid *A"B"C"D"*. How are the values in the ordered pairs affected by the translation?

h. If you were to translate trapezoid *ABCD* 10 units vertically to form trapezoid *DEFG*, what would be the ordered pairs of the corresponding vertices?

i. If you were to translate trapezoid *ABCD* 10 units horizontally to form trapezoid *HJKM*, what would be the ordered pairs of the corresponding vertices?

2. Recall that two geometric figures are considered congruent when they are the same size and the same shape.

a. Did sliding the trapezoid either up or down on the coordinate plane change the size or shape of the trapezoid?

b. Are both trapezoids congruent to the original trapezoid shown on the coordinate plane? Explain your reasoning.

7

Talk the Talk

1. Are all images, or new figures that result from a translation, always congruent to the original figure? Explain your reasoning.

2. For any real number *c* or *d*, describe how the ordered pair (*x*, *y*) of any original figure will change when translated:

   a. horizontally *c* units. How do you know if the image translated to the left or to the right?

   b. vertically *d* units. How do you know if the image translated up or down?

Remember, congruence preserves size and shape.

Be prepared to share your solutions and methods.

7.2 SLIDING LINES
Translations of Linear Functions

Learning Goals

In this lesson, you will:

▶ Translate linear functions horizontally and vertically.

▶ Use multiple representations such as tables, graphs, and equations to represent linear functions and the translations of linear functions.

Look at the lines below each row of black and white squares. Are these lines straight? Grab a ruler or other straightedge to test.

This very famous optical illusion is called the Zöllner illusion, named after its discoverer, Johann Karl Friedrich Zöllner, who first wrote about it in 1860.

7

Problem 1   Translating Linear Functions Up or Down

In the previous lesson, geometric figures were translated vertically (up or down) and horizontally (left or right). In this lesson, you will use that knowledge to translate linear functions both vertically and horizontally.

1. Consider the equation $y = x$. Complete the table of values.

x	y
−3	
−2	
−1	
0	
1	
2	
3	

How do you know that y = x is a function?

2. Use the table of values and the coordinate plane provided to graph the equation $y = x$.

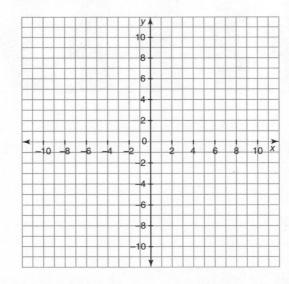

3. Did you connect the points on the graph of the equation? Why or why not?

4. In the previous lesson, a geometric figure was translated down 4 units.

   a. How did that affect the value of the *x*-coordinate of each vertex?

   b. How did that affect the value of the *y*-coordinate of each vertex?

5. Use your experience of translating a geometric figure to translate the graph of $y = x$ down 4 units. Draw the new line on the coordinate plane in Question 2 and then complete the table of values.

x	y
−3	
−2	
−1	
0	
1	
2	
3	

How will this table of values compare to the table in Question 1?

6. Compare the graph of $y = x$ to the graph of $y = x$ translated down 4 units.

   a. What do you notice?

   b. Write an equation in the form $y =$ to represent the translation.

Are the two equations the same?

   c. Write an equation in the form $x =$ to represent the translation.

7. Translate the graph of $y = x$ up 4 units. Draw the new line on the coordinate plane in Question 2 and then complete the table of values.

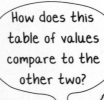

How does this table of values compare to the other two?

x	y
−3	
−2	
−1	
0	
1	
2	
3	

8. Compare the graph of $y = x$ to the graph of $y = x$ translated up 4 units.

    a. What do you notice?

    b. Write an equation in the form $y =$ to represent the translation.

    c. Write an equation in the form $x =$ to represent the translation.

9. Label each equation on the coordinate plane in slope-intercept form. What do you notice? What is similar about each line? What is different?

Problem 2   Translating Linear Functions Left or Right

1. In the previous lesson, a geometric figure was translated to the left 4 units.

    a. How did that affect the value of the x-coordinate of each vertex?

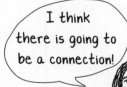

I think there is going to be a connection!

    b. How did that affect the value of the y-coordinate of each vertex?

2. Graph the equation $y = x$ on the coordinate plane.

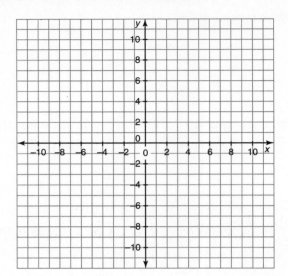

3. Use your experience of translating a geometric figure to translate the graph of $y = x$ to the left 4 units. Draw the new line on the coordinate plane and then complete the table of values.

x	y
	−3
	−2
	−1
	0
	1
	2
	3

4. Compare the graph of $y = x$ to the graph of $y = x$ translated to the left 4 units.

   a. What do you notice?

b. Write an equation in the form *y* = to represent the translation.

c. Write an equation in the form *x* = to represent the translation.

5. Translate the graph of *y* = *x* to the right 4 units. Draw the new line on the coordinate plane in Question 2 and then complete the table of values.

x	y
	−3
	−2
	−1
	0
	1
	2
	3

6. Compare the graph of *y* = *x* to the graph of *y* = *x* translated to the right 4 units.

a. What do you notice?

b. Write an equation in the form *y* = to represent the translation.

c. Write an equation in the form *x* = to represent the translation.

7. Label each equation on the coordinate plane in slope-intercept form. What do you notice? What is similar about each line? What is different?

7

Problem 3 Making Connections

1. Organize the equations you determined for the graph of each translation performed on the linear equation $y = x$ in the previous problem by completing the last two columns of the table shown.

Original Equation	Translation Performed	Equation of Translation in the Form of $y =$	Equation of Translation in the Form of $x =$
$y = x$	Down 4 Units	$y =$	$x =$
$y = x$	Up 4 Units	$y =$	$x =$
$y = x$	Left 4 Units	$y =$	$x =$
$y = x$	Right 4 Units	$y =$	$x =$

2. Which translations of the linear equation $y = x$ resulted in the same graph?

3. Kieran says that whenever a linear equation written in slope-intercept form shows a plus sign, it is a translation right or up, and when it shows a minus sign it is a translation left or down, because positive always means up and right on the coordinate grid, and negative always means left and down. Is Kieran correct? Justify your answer.

4. Each graph shown is a result of a translation performed on the equation $y = x$. Describe the translation. Then write an equation in slope-intercept form.

a.

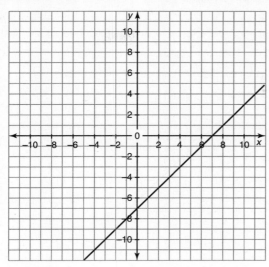

b.

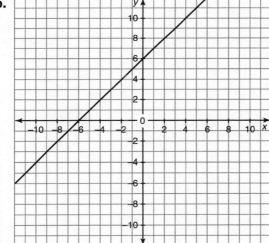

5. Each graph shown is a result of a translation performed on the equation $y = -x$. Describe the translation.

a.

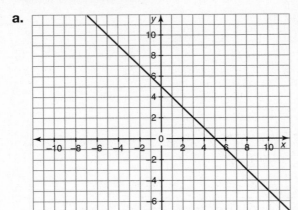

b.

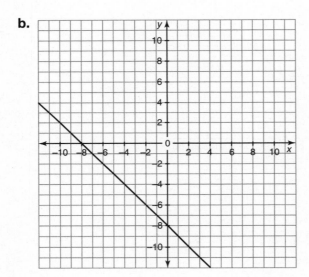

6. Each equation shown is a result of a translation performed on the equation $y = x$. Describe the translation.

a. $y = x + 12.5$

b. $y = x - 15.25$

7. Each equation shown is a result of a translation performed on the equation $y = -x$. Describe the translation.

   a. $y = -x - 1.2$

   b. $y = -x + 3.8$

Talk the Talk

1. The equation shown is a result of a translation performed on the equation $y = x$. For any real number h, describe the possible translations.

   $y = x + h$

2. The equation shown is a result of a translation performed on the equation $y = -x$. For any real number h, describe the possible translations.

   $y = -x + h$

3. If a function is translated horizontally or vertically, is the resulting line still a function?

Be prepared to share your solutions and methods.

7

7

7.3 ROUND AND ROUND WE GO!

Rotations of Geometric Figures on the Coordinate Plane

Learning Goal

In this lesson, you will:

▶ Rotate geometric figures on the coordinate plane.

Key Terms

▶ rotation
▶ angle of rotation
▶ point of rotation

Centrifuges are devices that spin material around a center point. Centrifuges are used in biology and chemistry, often to separate materials in a gas or liquid.

Tubes are inserted into the device and, as it spins, heavier material is pushed to the bottom of the tubes while lighter material tends to rise to the top.

Human centrifuges are used to test pilots and astronauts. Can you think of other devices that work like centrifuges?

7

Problem 1   What Is a Rotation?

You have considered what happens to shapes when you slide them up, down, left, or right. Let's explore what happens when you rotate a geometric figure.

1. Look at the triangles shown in the coordinate plane.

Grab your shapes from the first lesson.

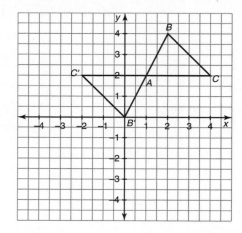

2. Place your triangle on △*ABC*. Without moving vertex *A*, "transform" the triangle into △*AB'C'*.

3. Describe how you transformed the triangle.

Notice the triangles share a vertex.

4. Katie says that she can use translations to move triangle *ABC* to triangle *AB'C'*. Is she correct? Explain your reasoning.

7

A **rotation** is a transformation that turns a figure about a fixed point for a given angle, called the *angle of rotation*, and a given direction. The **angle of rotation** is the amount of rotation about a fixed point, or **point of rotation**. Rotation can be clockwise or counterclockwise.

The point of rotation can be a point on the figure.

Or, it can be a point not on the figure.

The point of rotation stays fixed.

It can also be a point in the figure.

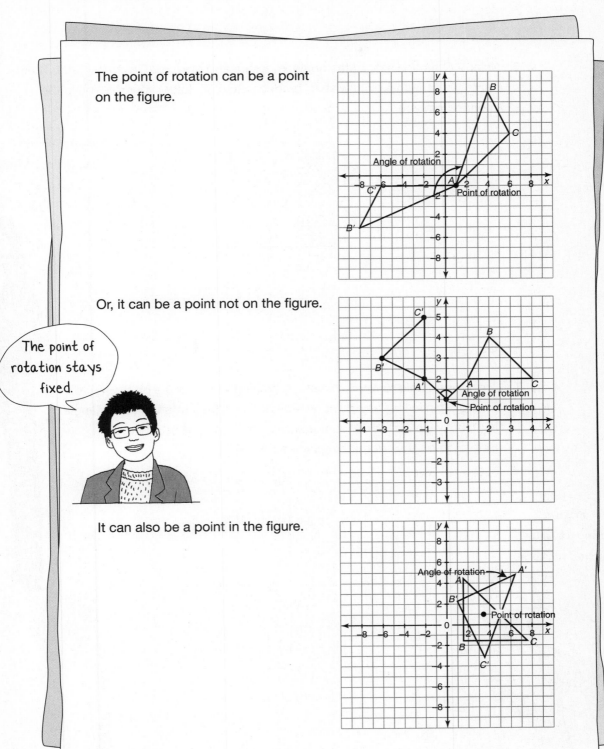

5. Use your triangle to rotate △ABC in Question 1 by placing your triangle on the figure, putting a pin in it at vertex C, and then rotating your triangle first to the left and then to the right.

6. Using $\overline{AC}$ as one side of the angle, measure and draw ∠ACA′ to be 120°. Then, rotate your triangle clockwise to produce △CA′B′. Label your rotation in the coordinate plane.

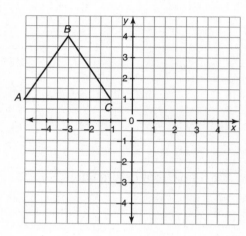

You will need your protractor.

7. Use your triangle to rotate △ABC by placing your triangle on the figure, putting a pin in it at any point on side $\overline{AC}$, and then rotating your triangle first clockwise and then counterclockwise. Trace one rotation you performed on the coordinate plane as △A″B″C″.

Place a point at your point of rotation.

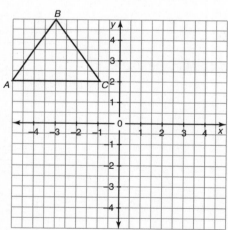

8. Recall that two geometric figures are considered congruent when they are the same size and the same shape.

   a. Did rotating the triangle on the coordinate plane in any of the previous questions change the size or shape of the triangle?

   b. Is the image of the triangle that resulted from the rotation congruent to the triangle shown on the coordinate plane? Explain your reasoning.

Problem 2   Rotating a Parallelogram

1. Use your parallelogram to rotate parallelogram *ABCD* by placing your parallelogram on the figure, putting a pin in it at any point in the interior of the parallelogram, and then rotating your parallelogram first clockwise and then counterclockwise. Trace one rotation you performed on the coordinate plane. Place a point at your center of rotation.

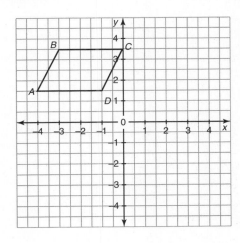

Does the shape change size when I rotate it?

2. Recall that two geometric figures are considered congruent when they are the same size and the same shape.

    a. Did rotating the parallelogram on the coordinate plane change the size or shape of the parallelogram?

    b. Is the image of the parallelogram that resulted from the rotation congruent to the parallelogram shown on the coordinate plane? Explain your reasoning.

Problem 3   Rotating a Trapezoid

1. Use your trapezoid to rotate trapezoid *ABCD* around point *P* by placing your trapezoid on the figure. Fold a piece of tape in half and tape it to both sides of the trapezoid, making sure that the tape covers point *P*. Put a pin in at point *P*, and rotate your parallelogram first clockwise and then counterclockwise. Trace one rotation you performed on the coordinate plane.

Don't tape your trapezoid to your paper!

2. Recall that two geometric figures are considered congruent when they are the same size and the same shape.

a. Did rotating the trapezoid on the coordinate plane change the size or shape of the trapezoid?

b. Is the image of the trapezoid congruent to the trapezoid shown on the coordinate plane? Explain your reasoning.

Talk the Talk

1. Are all images, or new figures that result from a rotation, always congruent to the original figure? Explain your reasoning.

2. Describe the point of rotation in each.

a.

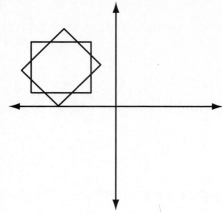

b.

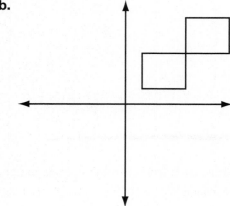

So is the point of rotation in the figure, on the figure, or not on the figure?

c.

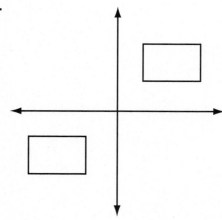

Be prepared to share your solutions and methods.

MIRROR, MIRROR
Reflections of Geometric Figures on the Coordinate Plane

Learning Goals

In this lesson, you will:

▶ Reflect geometric figures over the axes on the coordinate plane.

▶ Reflect geometric figures over lines on the coordinate plane.

Key Terms

▶ reflection

▶ reflection line

The astronauts aboard the Apollo Moon missions in 1969 through the 1970s did more than just play golf and take pictures. They also set up equipment on the Moon to help scientists measure the distance from the Moon to the Earth.

This equipment contained sets of mirrors, called retroreflectors. Scientists on Earth can now shoot laser beams at these mirrors and calculate the distance to the Moon by observing how long it takes the laser beam to "bounce back."

7

Problem 1   Reflections Over the Axes

In this lesson you will explore what happens to geometric figures that are reflected over different lines.

1. Look at the two triangles shown in the coordinate plane.

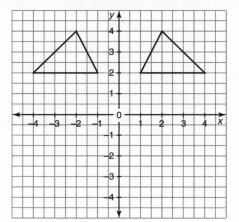

> If mirrors are not available, you can cut out a copy of the grid, fold it at the y-axis, and place it on the axis.

a. Describe the positions of the two triangles on this coordinate plane. Do you think the two triangles are congruent?

b. Place a mirror on the *y*-axis facing to the left. Describe what you see when you look at the triangle in the mirror.

c. Place a mirror on the *y*-axis facing to the right. Describe what you see when you look at the triangle in the mirror.

Figures that are mirror images of each other are called *reflections*. A **reflection** is a transformation that "flips" a figure over a *reflection line*. A **reflection line** is a line that acts as a mirror so that corresponding points are the same distance from the mirror. In this coordinate plane, either triangle is a reflection of the other.

d. What do you think is the reflection line in the diagram shown?

e. Draw the reflection of each of the triangles over the *x*-axis.

Imagine folding the coordinate plane at the x-axis.

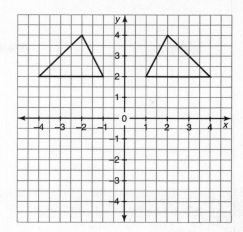

Be sure to use a straightedge.

2. Reflect parallelogram *ABCD*, using the *y*-axis as the reflection line, to form parallelogram *A′B′C′D′*.

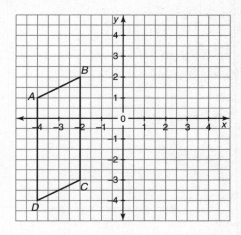

a. Connect each vertex of the original parallelogram to the corresponding vertex of the image with line segments $\overline{AA'}$, $\overline{BB'}$, $\overline{CC'}$, and $\overline{DD'}$.

b. Describe the relationship between the *y*-axis and each of the segments you drew.

7

You might want to create a table to organize your ordered pairs.

c. List the ordered pairs for the vertices of parallelogram *ABCD* and parallelogram *A'B'C'D'*.

d. What do you notice about the ordered pairs of the vertices of the original figure and its reflection over the *y*-axis?

3. Reflect parallelogram *ABCD* over the *x*-axis by using the *x*-axis as a perpendicular bisector.

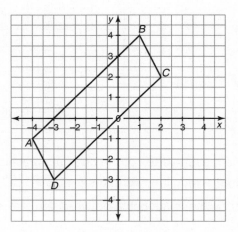

a. List the ordered pairs for the vertices of the original parallelogram and the reflected image.

b. What do you notice about the ordered pairs of the vertices of the original figure and its reflection over the *x*-axis?

4. A triangle has vertices at *A*(−4, 3), *B*(1, 5), *C*(2, −2).

   a. If this triangle is reflected over the *x*-axis, what would the ordered pairs of the reflection's vertices be?

   b. If this triangle is reflected over the *y*-axis, what would the ordered pairs of the reflection's vertices be?

Problem 2   Reflections Over Horizontal and Vertical Lines

1. Reflect the triangle over the line *x* = −1.

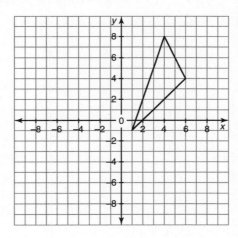

Draw the line x = -1 first.

2. Reflect the triangle over the line $y = 2$.

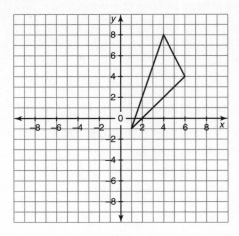

3. Recall that geometric figures are considered congruent when they are the same size and the same shape.

    a. Did reflecting the triangle on the coordinate plane change the size or shape of the figure?

    b. Is the image of the reflection of the triangle congruent to the original figure shown on the coordinate plane? Explain your reasoning.

Talk the Talk

1. Are all images, or new figures that result from a reflection, always congruent to the original figure? Explain.

2. Describe the line of reflection in each.

   a.

   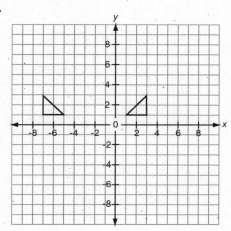

   b.

   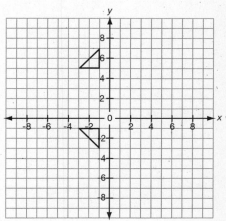

Be prepared to share your solutions and methods.

Key Terms

- transformation (7.1)
- translation (7.1)
- image (7.1)
- pre-image (7.1)
- rotation (7.3)

- angle of rotation (7.3)
- point of rotation (7.3)
- reflection (7.4)
- reflection line (7.4)

7.1   Translating Geometric Figures

A translation is a transformation that "slides" each point of a figure the same distance and direction. Sliding a figure left or right is a horizontal translation and sliding it up or down is a vertical translation. The new figure created from a translation is called the image.

Example

$\triangle ABC$ with coordinates $A(-2, 2)$, $B(0, 5)$, and $C(1, 1)$ is translated six units horizontally and -4 units vertically.

The coordinates of the image are $A'(4, -2)$, $B'(6, 1)$, and $C'(7, -3)$.

Feel like you still don't understand [some]thing new? That's OK. [As]k questions, practice [mo]re problems, and get involved. You will [u]nderstand it better after you do!

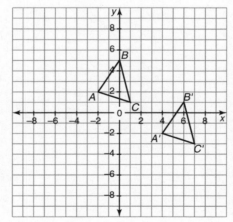

7.2 Translating Linear Functions

You learned that a translation is a transformation that "slides" each point of a geometric figure the same distance and direction. That knowledge can also be applied to linear functions on a coordinate plane.

Example

Complete the table of values using the function $y = x$.

x	y
−2	−2
−1	−1
1	1
2	2

Graph the function using the table of values.

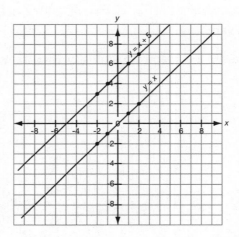

Translate the graph of $y = x$ up 5 units and complete the table of values.

x	y
−2	3
−1	4
1	6
2	7

Write an equation in the form $y =$ to represent the translation.

$y = x + 5$

7.3 Rotating Geometric Figures on a Coordinate Plane

A rotation is a transformation that turns a figure about a fixed point for a given angle and a given direction. The given angle is called the angle of rotation. The angle of rotation is the amount of rotation about a fixed point. The point around which the figure is rotated is called the point of rotation. Rotations can be either clockwise or counterclockwise.

Example

To rotate △XYZ 45° clockwise around point Z, use a protractor to draw a 45° angle as shown, with point Z as the vertex. Next, rotate the figure clockwise around point Z until the side corresponding to $\overline{YZ}$ has been rotated 45°. The image is labeled as △X'Y'Z.

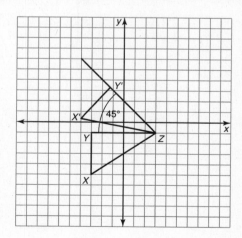

7.4 Reflecting Geometric Figures on the Coordinate Plane

A reflection is a transformation that "flips" a figure over a reflection line. A reflection line is a line that acts as a mirror such that corresponding points in the figure and its image are the same distance from the line.

When a figure is reflected over the x-axis, the y-values of the points on the image have the opposite sign of the y-values of the corresponding points on the original figure while the x-values remain the same. When a figure is reflected over the y-axis, the x-values of the points on the image have the opposite sign of the x-values of the corresponding points on the original figure while the y-values remain the same.

Example

A square with vertices $P(-1, 5)$, $Q(2, 8)$, $R(5, 5)$, and $S(2, 2)$ is reflected over the x-axis.

To determine the vertices of the image, change the sign of the y-coordinates of the figure's vertices to find the y-coordinates of the image's vertices. The x-coordinates remain the same. The vertices of the image are $P'(-1, -5)$, $Q'(2, -8)$, $R'(5, -5)$, and $S'(2, -2)$.

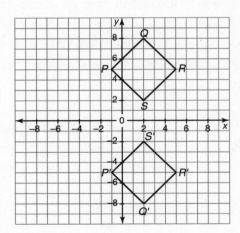

8 CONGRUENCE OF TRIANGLES

You've probably heard about identical twins, but do you know there's such a thing as mirror image twins? One mirror image twin is right-handed while the other is left-handed. And they could have birthmarks on opposite sides of their body. These calves sure look like mirror image twins!

SLIDE, FLIP, TURN!
Translations, Rotations, and Reflections of Triangles

8.1

8

Learning Goals

In this lesson, you will:

▶ Translate triangles in a coordinate plane.

▶ Rotate triangles in a coordinate plane.

▶ Reflect triangles in a coordinate plane.

When you look at the night sky, you see bright stars and dim stars. But are the dimmer stars farther away from us or just less bright? Astronomers use a variety of methods to measure the universe, but at the end of the 1980s, they made vast improvements in the accuracy of these measurements.

In 1989, the Hipparcos satellite was launched by the European Space Agency. Among other advantages, this satellite was not affected by Earth's atmosphere and could view the entire "sky," so it could provide more accurate measurements of distances. In 1997, the Hipparcos Catalogue was published, which contained high-precision distance information for more than 100,000 stars!

Problem 1   Translating Triangles in a Coordinate Plane

You have studied translations, rotations, and reflections of various geometric figures. In this lesson, you will explore, compare, and generalize the characteristics of triangles as you translate, rotate, and reflect them in a coordinate plane.

Consider the point (x, y) located anywhere in the first quadrant of the coordinate plane.

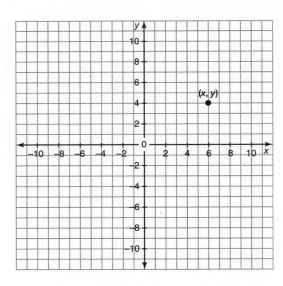

The ordered pair (x, y) represents any point that is located in the first quadrant.

1. Translate the point (x, y) according to the descriptions in the table shown. Plot the point, and then record the coordinates of the translated points in terms of x and y.

Translation	Point (x, y) located in Q1
3 units to the left	
3 units down	
3 units to the right	
3 units up	

2. Describe the translation in terms of x and y that would move any point (x, y) into:

   a. Quadrant II

   b. Quadrant III

Can you translate a point from QI to QIII in one move?

   c. Quadrant IV

3. Graph triangle ABC by plotting the points $A(-3, 4)$, $B(-6, 1)$, and $C(-4, 9)$.

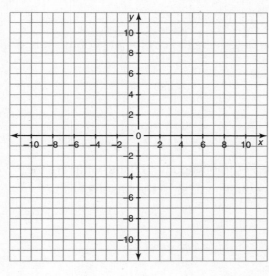

Triangle ABC is located in Quadrant II. Do you think any of these translations will change the quadrant location of the triangle?

Use the table to record the coordinates of the vertices of each triangle.

   a. Translate triangle ABC 5 units to the right to form triangle $A'B'C'$. List the coordinates of points A', B', and C'. Then graph triangle $A'B'C'$.

   b. Translate triangle ABC 8 units down to form triangle $A''B''C''$. List the coordinates of points A'', B'', and C''. Then graph triangle $A''B''C''$.

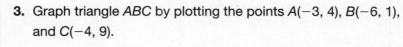

Original Triangle	Triangle Translated 5 units to the Right	Triangle Translated 8 units Down
△ABC	△A'B'C'	△A"B"C"
A (−3, 4)		
B (−6, 1)		
C (−4, 9)		

Let's consider the vertices of a different triangle and translations without graphing.

4. The vertices of triangle *DEF* are *D*(−7, 10), *E*(−5, 5), and *F*(−8, 1).

   a. If triangle *DEF* is translated to the right 12 units, what are the coordinates of the vertices of the image? Name the triangle.

   b. How did you determine the coordinates of the image without graphing the triangle?

Think about which values of the ordered pairs are changing.

   c. If triangle *DEF* is translated up 9 units, what are the coordinates of the vertices of the image? Name the triangle.

Create a table if it helps you organize the vertices.

   d. How did you determine the coordinates of the image without graphing the triangle?

Problem 2 Rotating Triangles in a Coordinate Plane

1. Graph the point (x, y) anywhere in the first quadrant of the coordinate plane.

Use your straightedge when drawing the 90° angle.

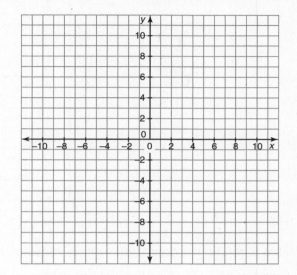

Use the table to record the coordinates of each point.

a. Using the origin $(0, 0)$ as the point of rotation, rotate point (x, y) 90° counterclockwise about the origin and graph the rotated point on the coordinate plane. What are the new coordinates of the rotated point in terms of x and y?

If your point was at (5, 0), and you rotated it 90°, where would it end up? What about if it was at (5, 1)?

b. Using the origin $(0, 0)$ as the point of rotation, rotate point (x, y) 180° counterclockwise about the origin and graph the rotated point on the coordinate plane. What are the new coordinates of the rotated point in terms of x and y?

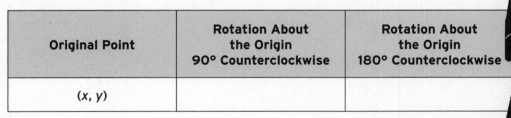

Original Point	Rotation About the Origin 90° Counterclockwise	Rotation About the Origin 180° Counterclockwise
(x, y)		

2. Graph triangle ABC by plotting the points $A(3, 4)$, $B(6, 1)$, and $C(4, 9)$.

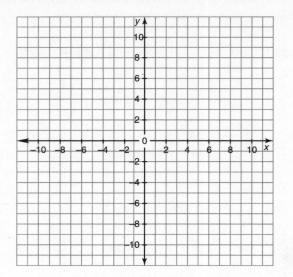

Think about your answers from Question 1 as you rotate the triangle.

Use the table to record the coordinates of the vertices of each triangle.

a. Using the origin (0, 0) as the point of rotation, rotate triangle ABC 90° counterclockwise about the origin to form triangle $A'B'C'$. Graph the triangle and then list the coordinates of the rotated triangle.

b. Using the origin (0, 0) as the point of rotation, rotate triangle ABC 180° counterclockwise about the origin to form triangle $A''B''C''$. Graph the triangle and then list the coordinates of the rotated triangle.

Original Triangle	Rotation About the Origin 90° Counterclockwise	Rotation About the Origin 180° Counterclockwise
△ABC	△$A'B'C'$	△$A''B''C''$
A (3, 4)		
B (6, 1)		
C (4, 9)		

Let's consider a different triangle and rotations without graphing.

3. The vertices of triangle *DEF* are *D*(−7, 10), *E*(−5, 5), and *F*(−1, −8).

   a. If triangle *DEF* is rotated 90° counterclockwise, what are the coordinates of the vertices of the image? Name the rotated triangle.

   b. How did you determine the coordinates of the image without graphing the triangle?

   c. If triangle *DEF* is rotated 180° counterclockwise, what are the coordinates of the vertices of the image? Name the rotated triangle.

   d. How did you determine the coordinates of the image without graphing the triangle?

1. Graph the point (x, y) anywhere in the first quadrant of the coordinate plane.

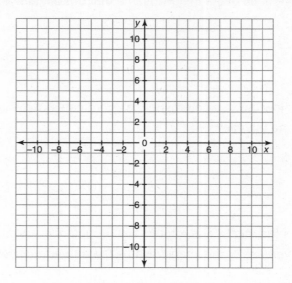

Use the table to record the coordinates of each point.

    a. Reflect and graph the point (x, y) over the x-axis on the coordinate plane. What are the new coordinates of the reflected point in terms of x and y?

    b. Reflect and graph the point (x, y) over the y-axis on the coordinate plane. What are the new coordinates of the reflected point in terms of x and y?

Original Point	Reflection Over the x-axis	Reflection Over the y-axis
(x, y)		

2. Graph triangle *ABC* by plotting the points *A*(3, 4), *B*(6, 1), and *C*(4, 9).

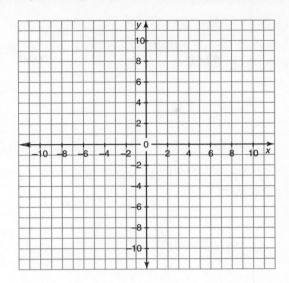

Use the table to record the coordinates of the vertices of each triangle.

a. Reflect triangle *ABC* over the *x*-axis to form triangle *A'B'C'*. Graph the triangle and then list the coordinates of the reflected triangle.

b. Reflect triangle *ABC* over the *y*-axis to form triangle *A"B"C"*. Graph the triangle and then list the coordinates of the reflected triangle.

Original Triangle	Triangle Reflected Over the *x*-axis	Triangle Reflected Over the *y*-axis
△*ABC*	△*A'B'C'*	△*A"B"C"*
A (3, 4)		
B (6, 1)		
C (4, 9)		

Do you see any patterns?

Let's consider a different triangle and reflections without graphing.

3. The vertices of triangle *DEF* are *D*(−7, 10), *E*(−5, 5), and *F*(−1, −8).

    a. If triangle *DEF* is reflected over the *x*-axis, what are the coordinates of the vertices of the image? Name the triangle.

    b. How did you determine the coordinates of the image without graphing the triangle?

    c. If triangle *DEF* is reflected over the *y*-axis, what are the coordinates of the vertices of the image? Name the triangle.

    d. How did you determine the coordinates of the image without graphing the triangle?

Talk the Talk

1. The vertices of triangle *PQR* are *P*(4, 3), *Q*(−2, 2), and *R*(0, 0). Describe the translation used to form each triangle. Explain your reasoning.

   a. *P′*(0, 3), *Q′*(−6, 2), and *R′*(−4, 0)

   b. *P″*(4, 5.5), *Q″*(−2, 4.5), and *R″*(0, 2.5)

2. The vertices of triangle *JME* are *J*(1, 3), *M*(6, 5), and *E*(8, 1). Describe the rotation used to form each triangle. Explain your reasoning.

   a. *J′*(−3, 1), *M′*(−5, 6), and *E′*(−1, 8)

   b. *J″*(−1, −3), *M″*(−6, −5), and *E″*(−8, −1)

3. The vertices of triangle *NRT* are *N*(12, 4), *R*(14, 1), and *T*(20, 9). Describe the reflection used to form each triangle. Explain your reasoning.

   a. *N*′(−12, 4), *R*′(−14, 1), and *T*′(−20, 9)

   b. *N*″(12, −4), *R*″(14, −1), and *T*″(20, −9)

4. Are all the images that result from a translation, rotation, or reflection (always, sometimes, or never) congruent to the original figure?

> Remember, congruence preserves size and shape.

Be prepared to share your solutions and methods.

8.2 ALL THE SAME TO YOU
Congruent Triangles

Learning Goals

In this lesson, you will:

▶ Identify corresponding sides and corresponding angles of congruent triangles.

▶ Explore the relationship between corresponding sides of congruent triangles.

▶ Explore the relationship between corresponding angles of congruent triangles.

▶ Write statements of triangle congruence.

▶ Identify and use transformations to create new images.

Key Terms

▶ congruent line segments
▶ congruent angles
▶ corresponding sides
▶ corresponding angles

In mathematics, when a geometric figure is translated, reflected, or rotated, the size and shape of the figure doesn't change. But in physics, things are a little different. An idea called length contraction in physics means that when an object is in motion, its length appears to be slightly less than it really is. The faster the object is moving, the smaller it appears. If an object is moving at the speed of light, it would be practically invisible!

Problem 1   Understanding Congruence

In the previous lesson, you determined that if a triangle was translated, rotated, or reflected, it resulted in creating an image that was the same size and the same shape as the original triangle; therefore, the image and the original triangle are said to be congruent triangles.

Congruent line segments are line segments that have the same length. Congruent triangles are triangles that are the same size and the same shape.

If the length of line segment *AB* is equal to the length of line segment *DE*, the relationship can be expressed using symbols. These are a few examples.

- *AB* = *DE* is read "the distance between *A* and *B* is equal to the distance between *D* and *E*"

- *m$\overline{AB}$* = *m$\overline{DE}$* is read "the measure of line segment *AB* is equal to the measure of line segment *DE*."

If the sides of two different triangles are equal in length, for example, the length of side *AB* in triangle *ABC* is equal to the length of side *DE* in triangle *DEF*, these sides are said to be congruent. This relationship can be expressed using symbols.

- $\overline{AB} \cong \overline{DE}$ is read "line segment *AB* is congruent to line segment *DE*."

Congruent angles are angles that are equal in measure.

If the measure of angle *A* is equal to the measure of angle *D*, the relationship can be expressed using symbols.

- *m∠A* = *m∠D* is read "the measure of angle *A* is equal to the measure of angle *D*."

If the angles of two different triangles are equal in measure, for example, the measure of angle *A* in triangle *ABC* is equal to the measure of angle *D* in triangle *DEF*, these angles are said to be congruent. This relationship can be expressed using symbols.

- ∠A ≅ ∠D is read "angle *A* is congruent to angle *D*."

Problem 2 Corresponding Sides of Congruent Triangles

Let's explore the properties of congruent triangles.

1. Graph triangle *ABC* by plotting the points *A*(8, 10), *B*(1, 2), and *C*(8, 2).

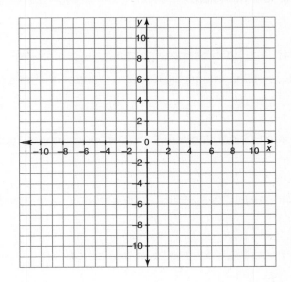

a. Describe triangle *ABC*.

b. Use the coordinate plane to determine the lengths of sides *AC* and *BC*.

c. Use the Pythagorean Theorem to determine the length of side *AB*.

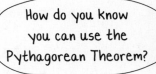

How do you know you can use the Pythagorean Theorem?

2. Translate triangle *ABC* 10 units to the left to form triangle *DEF*. Graph triangle *DEF* and list the coordinates of points *D*, *E*, and *F*.

Corresponding sides are sides that have the same relative positions in geometric figures.

Triangle *ABC* and triangle *DEF* in Question 1 are the same size and the same shape. Each side in triangle *ABC* matches or corresponds to a specific side in triangle *DEF*.

3. What would you predict to be true about the lengths of corresponding sides of congruent triangles?

4. Identify the pairs of corresponding sides of triangle *ABC* and triangle *DEF*.

   a. Side *AC* in triangle *ABC* corresponds to what side in triangle *DEF*?

   b. Side *BC* in triangle *ABC* corresponds to what side in triangle *DEF*?

   c. Side *AB* in triangle *ABC* corresponds to what side in triangle *DEF*?

5. Determine the side lengths of triangle *DEF*.

   a. $m\overline{DF}$

   b. $m\overline{EF}$

   c. $m\overline{DE}$

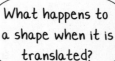

What happens to a shape when it is translated?

6. Compare the lengths of the sides in triangle *ABC* to the lengths of the corresponding sides in triangle *DEF*.

   a. How does the length of side *AC* compare to the length of side *DF*?

   b. How does the length of side *BC* compare to the length of side *EF*?

   c. How does the length of side *AB* compare to the length of side *DE*?

7. In general, what can be said about the relationship between the corresponding sides of congruent triangles?

Problem 3   Corresponding Angles of Congruent Triangles

Use triangle *ABC* and triangle *DEF* in Problem 2 to answer each question.

1. Use a protractor to determine the measure of angles *A*, *B*, and *C*.

Triangle *ABC* and triangle *DEF* are the same size and the same shape. Each angle in triangle *ABC* matches, or corresponds, to a specific angle in triangle *DEF*. **Corresponding angles** are angles that have the same relative positions in geometric figures.

2. What would you predict to be true about the measures of corresponding angles of congruent triangles?

3. Identify the corresponding angles of triangle *ABC* and triangle *DEF*.

   a. Angle *A* in triangle *ABC* corresponds to what angle in triangle *DEF*?

   b. Angle *B* in triangle *ABC* corresponds to what angle in triangle *DEF*?

   c. Angle *C* in triangle *ABC* corresponds to what angle in triangle *DEF*?

4. Use a protractor to determine the measures of angles *D*, *E*, and *F*.

5. Compare the measures of the angles in triangle *ABC* to the measures of the corresponding angles in triangle *DEF*.

   a. How does the measure of angle *A* compare to the measure of angle *D*?

   b. How does the measure of angle *B* compare to the measure of angle *E*?

So, what can you say about corresponding sides and corresponding angles of congruent triangles?

   c. How does the measure of angle *C* compare to the measure of angle *F*?

6. In general, what can be said about the relationship between the corresponding angles of congruent triangles?

Problem 4   Statements of Triangle Congruence

1. Consider the congruence statement △*JRB* ≅ △*MNS*.

   a. Identify the congruent angles.   **b.** Identify the congruent sides.

So, if you know that two angles are congruent then you also know their measures are equal.

2. Analyze the two triangles shown.

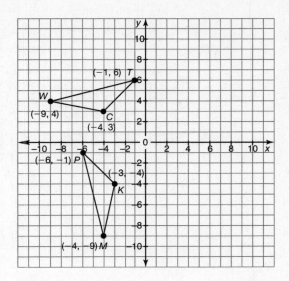

a. Identify the transformation used to create triangle *PMK*.

b. Does the transformation used preserve the size and shape of the triangle?

c. Using the triangles shown, write a triangle congruence statement.

d. Using your congruence statement, identify the congruent angles.

e. Using your congruence statement, identify the congruent sides.

3. Analyze the two triangles shown.

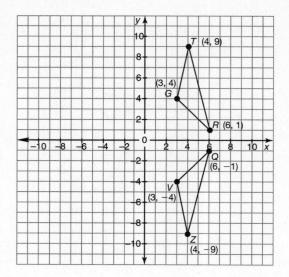

a. Identify the transformation used to create triangle *ZQV*.

b. Does the transformation used preserve the size and shape of the triangle?

c. Using the triangles shown, write a triangle congruence statement.

d. Using your congruence statement, identify the congruent angles.

e. Using your congruence statement, identify the congruent sides.

Talk the Talk

1. Given any triangle in a coordinate plane, how can you create a different triangle that you know will be congruent to the original triangle?

2. Describe the properties of congruent triangles.

Be prepared to share your solutions and methods.

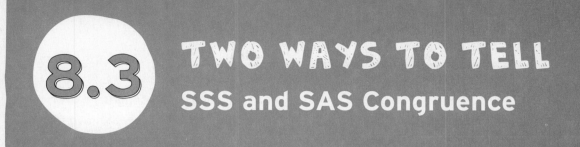

8.3 TWO WAYS TO TELL
SSS and SAS Congruence

Learning Goals

In this lesson, you will:

▶ Explore the SSS Congruence Theorem.

▶ Explore the SAS Congruence Theorem.

▶ Use the SSS and SAS Congruence Theorems to identify congruent triangles.

Key Terms

▶ SSS Congruence Theorem

▶ included angle

▶ SAS Congruence Theorem

The smaller circle you see here has an infinite number of points. And the larger circle has an infinite number of points. But since the larger circle is, well, larger, shouldn't it have *more* points than the smaller circle?

Mathematicians use one-to-one correspondence to tell if two sets are equal. If you can show that each object in a set corresponds to one and only one object in another set, then the two sets are equal.

Look at the circles. Any ray drawn from the center will touch only two points—one on the smaller circle and one on the larger circle. This means that both circles contain the same number of points! Can you see how correspondence was used to come up with this answer?

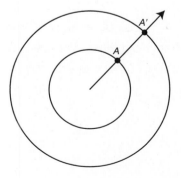

Problem 1   Three Sides

In the previous lesson, you determined that when two triangles are congruent, their corresponding angles and corresponding sides are congruent. To show that two triangles are congruent, do you think you would need to show that all of the pairs of corresponding sides and all of the pairs of corresponding angles are congruent? In this lesson, you will explore efficient methods for showing two triangles are congruent.

1. If the lengths of three sides of a triangle are known, do you think that is enough information to draw a congruent triangle? Let's explore this possibility.

   a. Use a straightedge to draw triangle *ABC* in the space provided.

   > You will need a straightedge and a protractor.

   b. Use a ruler to measure the length of each side, *AB*, *BC*, and *AC*, of triangle *ABC* and record the measurements.

   $m\overline{AB} =$ _____ $m\overline{BC} =$ _____ $m\overline{AC} =$ _____

   c. Use the measurements in part (b) to draw triangle *DEF* in the space provided.

   > Do you have to draw triangle DEF in the same orientation as triangle ABC?

   d. Based on your knowledge about the properties of congruent triangles, what other information is needed to determine if the two triangles are congruent? How can you acquire that information?

e. Determine the measurements to get the additional information needed and decide if the two triangles are congruent.

You have just shown that when all the side lengths of one triangle are equal to all the side lengths of another triangle, it is possible to determine that the two triangles are congruent. In the study of geometry, this method is expressed as a theorem.

The **Side-Side-Side (SSS) Congruence Theorem** states that if three sides of one triangle are congruent to the corresponding sides of another triangle, then the triangles are congruent.

2. Use the SSS Congruence Theorem to determine if the two triangles drawn on the coordinate plane are congruent.

If you know that corresponding parts of a triangle have equal measures then you can say they are congruent.

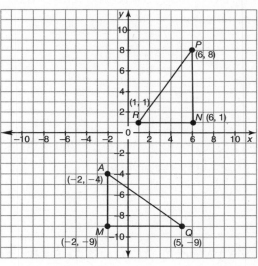

Be sure to write a final statement with your conclusion.

Problem 2   Two Sides and the Included Angle

If the lengths of two sides and the measure of the *included angle* of a triangle are known, do you think that is enough information to draw a congruent triangle? An **included angle** is the angle formed by two sides of a triangle. Let's explore this possibility.

1. Use a straightedge to draw triangle *ABC* in the space provided.

a. Use a ruler to measure the length of sides *AB* and *BC* of triangle *ABC* and record the measurements.

$m\overline{AB} =$ _____

$m\overline{BC} =$ _____

b. Use a protractor to measure ∠*B*, the included angle, and record the measurement.

$m\angle B =$ _____

c. Use the measurements in parts (b) and (c) to draw triangle *DEF* in the space provided.

So, the included angle depends on the sides. For any two sides, the included angle is the one "between" them.

d. Based on your knowledge about the properties of congruent triangles, what other information is needed to determine if the two triangles are congruent? How can you acquire that information?

e. Determine the measurements to get the additional information needed and decide if the two triangles are congruent.

You have just shown that when the measures of two sides and the included angle of one triangle are equal to the measures of two sides and the included angle of another triangle, it is possible to determine that the two triangles are congruent. In the study of geometry, this method is expressed as a theorem.

The **Side-Angle-Side (SAS) Congruence Theorem** states that if two sides and the included angle of one triangle are congruent to the corresponding two sides and the included angle of a second triangle, then the triangles are congruent.

2. Use the SAS Congruence Theorem and a protractor to determine if the two triangles drawn on the coordinate plane shown are congruent. Use a protractor to verify the measure of the included angle.

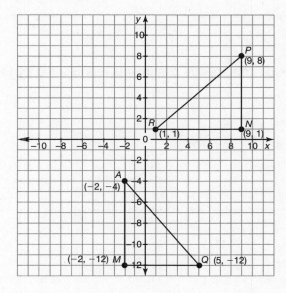

8

Congruent line segments and congruent angles are often denoted using some type of marker, rather than given measurements.

Slash markers can be used to convey congruent line segments. If line segments contain a single slash marker, this implies that all of those line segments are congruent, or equal in measure. Double and triple slash markers can also be used to denote other line segment congruencies.

Arc markers can be used to convey congruent angles. If angles contain a single arc marker, this implies that all of those angles are congruent, or equal in measure. Double and triple arc markers can also be used to denote other angle congruencies.

The markers on the diagram show congruent line segments.

$\overline{AB} \cong \overline{DF}$ and $\overline{BC} \cong \overline{ED}$

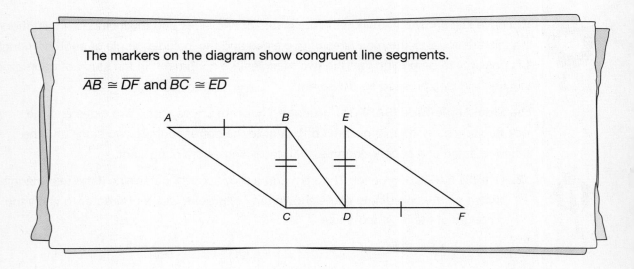

1. Write the congruence statements represented by the markers in each diagram.

   a.

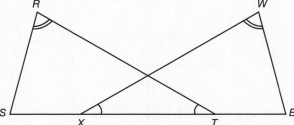

b.

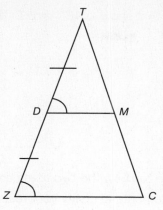

You can analyze diagrams and use SAS and SSS to determine if triangles are congruent.

Analyze the figure shown to determine if △*ABC* is congruent to △*DCB*.

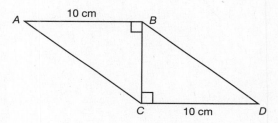

Notice, $m\overline{AB}$ = 10 cm and $m\overline{DC}$ = 10 cm and they are corresponding sides of each triangle. Also notice that ∠*ABC* and ∠*DCB* are right angles and they are corresponding angles of each triangle.

In order to prove the two triangles are congruent using SAS, you need to show another line segment of each triangle is congruent. Notice that the two triangles share a side. Because line segment *BC* is the same as line segment *CB*, you know that these two line segments are congruent.

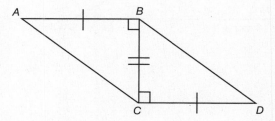

So, △*ABC* ≅ △*DCB* by the SAS Congruence Theorem.

2. Write the three congruence statements that show $\triangle ABC \cong \triangle DCB$ by the SAS Congruence Theorem.

3. Determine if there is enough information to show the two triangles are congruent by SSS or SAS. Write the congruence statements to justify your reasoning.

a. $\triangle ABC \overset{?}{\cong} \triangle ADC$

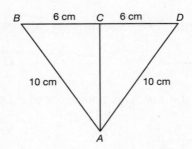

Use markers to identify all congruent line segments and angles.

b. $\triangle ABC \overset{?}{\cong} \triangle DEF$

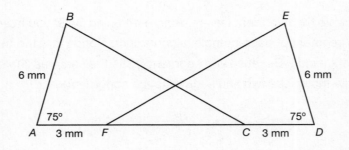

4. Simone says that since the two triangles below have two congruent corresponding sides and congruent corresponding angles, then the triangles are congruent by SAS. Is Simone correct? Explain your reasoning.

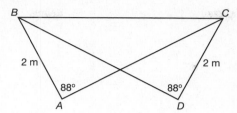

Be prepared to share your solutions and methods.

AND HERE'S TWO MORE!

ASA and AAS Congruence

Learning Goals

In this lesson, you will:

▶ Explore the ASA Congruence Theorem.

▶ Explore the AAS Congruence Theorem.

▶ Use the ASA and AAS Congruence Theorems to identify congruent triangles.

Key Terms

▶ included side

▶ ASA Congruence Theorem

▶ AAS Congruence Theorem

Which of the blue lines shown is longer? Most people will answer that the line on the right appears to be longer.

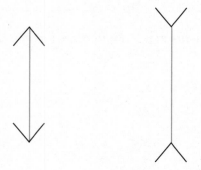

But in fact, both blue lines are the exact same length! This famous optical illusion is known as the Mueller-Lyer illusion. You can measure the lines to see for yourself. You can also draw some of your own to see how it almost always works!

Problem 1   Two Angles and the Included Side

In the previous lesson, you determined that two triangles are congruent if three pairs of corresponding sides are congruent (SSS), or if two pairs of corresponding sides and the included angles are congruent (SAS).

If the measures of two angles of a triangle and the length of the *included side* are known, do you think that is enough information to draw a congruent triangle? An **included side** is the line segment between two angles of a triangle. Let's explore this possibility.

1. Use a straightedge to draw triangle *ABC* in the space provided.

> Get out your straightedge and protractor.

a. Use a ruler to measure the length of side *AB*. Use a protractor to measure ∠*A* and ∠*B*. Record the measurements.

$m\overline{AB} =$ _____ $m\angle A =$ _____ $m\angle B =$ _____

b. Use the measurements in part (a) to draw triangle *DEF* in the space provided.

> Do you have to draw triangle DEF in the same orientation as triangle ABC?

c. Based on your knowledge about the properties of congruent triangles, what other information is needed to determine if the two triangles are congruent? How can you acquire that information?

d. Determine the measurements to get the additional information needed and decide if the two triangles are congruent.

You have just shown that when the measures of two angles and the included side of one triangle is equal to the measures of two angles and the included side of another triangle, it is possible to determine that the two triangles are congruent. In the study of geometry, this method is expressed as a theorem.

The **Angle-Side-Angle (ASA) Congruence Theorem** states that if two angles and the included side of one triangle are congruent to the corresponding two angles and the included side of another triangle, then the triangles are congruent.

2. Use the ASA Congruence Theorem and a protractor to determine if the two triangles drawn on the coordinate plane shown below are congruent.

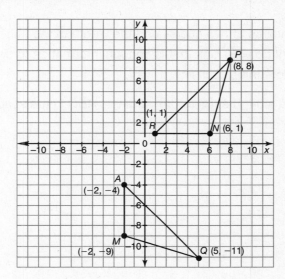

Problem 2   Two Angles and the Non-Included Side

8

1. How does knowing the location of an included side help you to understand the location of a non-included side? Explain your reasoning.

If the measures of two angles and the length of the non-included side of a triangle are known, do you think that is enough information to draw a congruent triangle? Let's explore this possibility.

2. Use a straightedge to draw triangle *ABC* in the space provided.

   a. Use a protractor to measure ∠*A* and ∠*B*, and a ruler to measure the length of *AC*, the non-included side. Record the measurements.

   $m\overline{AC}$ = _____ $m\angle A$ = _____ $m\angle B$ = _____

   b. Use the measurements in part (a) to draw triangle *DEF* in the space provided.

c. Based on your knowledge about the properties of congruent triangles, what other information is needed to determine if the two triangles are congruent, and how can you acquire that information?

d. Determine the measurements to get the additional information needed and decide if the two triangles are congruent.

You have just shown that when the measures of two angles and a non-included side of one triangle is equal to the measures of two angles and a non-included side of another triangle, it is possible to determine that the two triangles are congruent. In the study of geometry, this method is expressed as a theorem.

The **Angle-Angle-Side (AAS) Congruence Theorem** states that if two angles and a non-included side of one triangle are congruent to the corresponding angles and the corresponding non-included side of a second triangle, then the triangles are congruent.

3. Use the AAS Congruence Theorem and a protractor to determine if the two triangles drawn on the coordinate plane shown below are congruent. Use a protractor to verify the measure of the included angle.

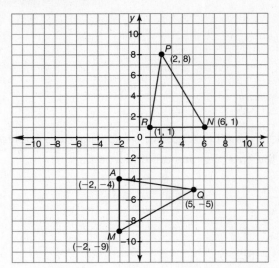

Problem 3　ASA Congruence or AAS Congruence

Determine if there is enough information to show the two triangles are congruent by ASA or AAS. Write the congruence statements to justify your reasoning.

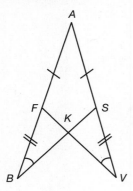
1. $\triangle ABS \overset{?}{\cong} \triangle AVF$

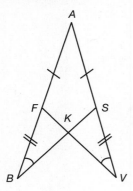

2. $\triangle GAB \overset{?}{\cong} \triangle SBA$

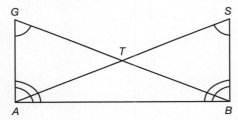

3. $\triangle EQD \overset{?}{\cong} \triangle DWE$

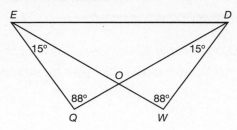

4. $\triangle ABC \overset{?}{\cong} \triangle PQR$

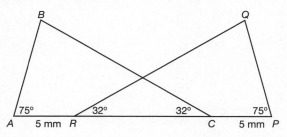

Use markers to show congruent sides and congruent angles.

Talk the Talk

This chapter focused on four methods to show that two triangles are congruent. Complete the graphic organizer by providing an illustration of each theorem.

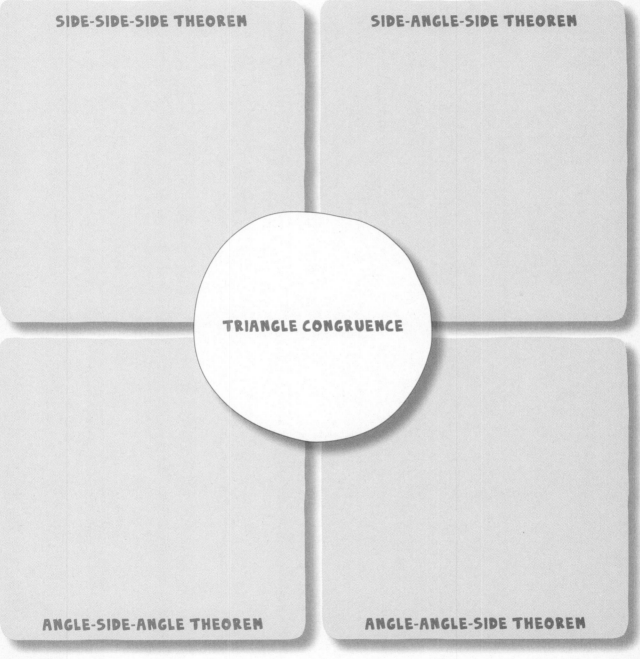

SIDE-SIDE-SIDE THEOREM

SIDE-ANGLE-SIDE THEOREM

TRIANGLE CONGRUENCE

ANGLE-SIDE-ANGLE THEOREM

ANGLE-ANGLE-SIDE THEOREM

Be prepared to share your solutions and methods.

8

Chapter 8   Summary

Key Terms

- congruent line segments (8.2)
- congruent angles (8.2)
- corresponding sides (8.2)
- corresponding angles (8.2)
- SSS Congruence Theorem (8.3)

- included angle (8.3)
- SAS Congruence Theorem (8.3)
- included side (8.4)
- ASA Congruence Theorem (8.4)
- AAS Congruence Theorem (8.4)

8.1 Translating Triangles in the Coordinate Plane

To translate a triangle in the coordinate plane means to move or "slide" the triangle to a new location without rotating it.

Example

Triangle ABC has been translated 10 units to the left and 2 units down to create triangle A'B'C'.

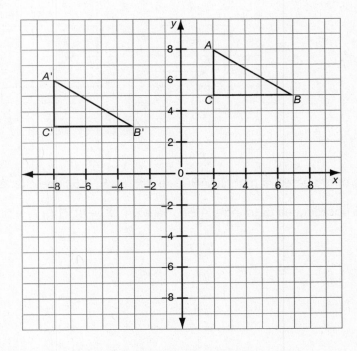

The coordinates of triangle ABC are A(2, 8), B(7, 5), and C(2, 5).

The coordinates of triangle A'B'C' are A'(−8, 6), B'(−3, 3), and C'(−8, 3).

8.1 Rotating Triangles in the Coordinate Plane

To rotate a triangle in the coordinate plane means to "turn" the triangle either clockwise or counterclockwise about a fixed point, which is usually the origin. To determine the new coordinates of a point after a 90° counterclockwise rotation, change the sign of the *y*-coordinate of the original point and then switch the *x*-coordinate and the *y*-coordinate. To determine the new coordinates of a point after a 180° rotation, change the signs of the *x*-coordinate and the *y*-coordinate of the original point.

Example

Triangle *ABC* has been rotated 180° counterclockwise about the origin to create triangle *A'B'C'*.

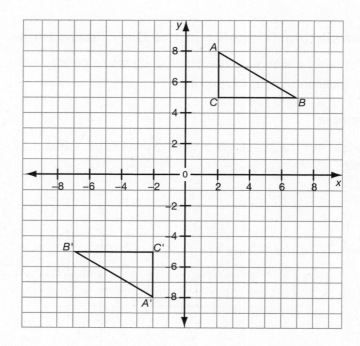

The coordinates of triangle *ABC* are *A*(2, 8), *B*(7, 5), and *C*(2, 5).

The coordinates of triangle *A'B'C'* are *A'*(−2, −8), *B'*(−7, −5), and *C'*(−2, −5).

Reflecting Triangles in a Coordinate Plane

To reflect a triangle in a coordinate plane means to "mirror" the triangle across a line of reflection to create a new triangle. Each point in the new triangle will be the same distance from the line of reflection as the corresponding point in the original triangle. To determine the coordinates of a point after a reflection across the *x*-axis, change the sign of the *y*-coordinate in the original point. To determine the coordinates of a point after a reflection across the *y*-axis, change the sign of the *x*-coordinate in the original point.

Example

Triangle *ABC* has been reflected across the *x*-axis to create triangle *A'B'C'*.

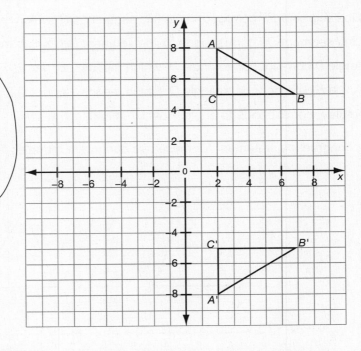

Keep learning! The more you think and the more you learn, the more your brain grows.

The coordinates of triangle *ABC* are *A*(2, 8), *B*(7, 5), and *C*(2, 5).

The coordinates of triangle *A'B'C'* are *A'*(2, −8), *B'*(7, −5), and *C'*(2, −5).

8.2 **Identifying Corresponding Sides and Angles of Congruent Triangles**

Congruent figures are figures that are the same size and the same shape. Congruent triangles are triangles that are the same size and the same shape. Congruent line segments are line segments that are equal in length. Congruent angles are angles that are equal in measure. In congruent figures, the corresponding angles are congruent and the corresponding sides are congruent.

Example

Triangle *DEF* has been reflected across the *y*-axis to create triangle *PQR*.

- Line segment *DE* corresponds to line segment *PQ*, which means $\overline{DE} \cong \overline{PQ}$.
- Line segment *EF* corresponds to line segment *QR*, which means $\overline{EF} \cong \overline{QR}$.
- Line segment *DF* corresponds to line segment *PR*, which means $\overline{DF} \cong \overline{PR}$.
- Angle *D* corresponds to angle *P*, which means $\angle D \cong \angle P$.
- Angle *E* corresponds to angle *Q*, which means $\angle E \cong \angle Q$.
- Angle *F* corresponds to angle *R*, which means $\angle F \cong \angle R$.

The congruence statement for these two congruent triangles is $\triangle DEF \cong \triangle PQR$.

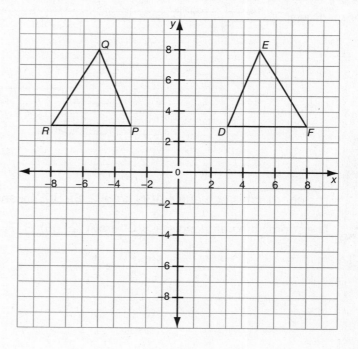

8.3

Using the SSS Congruence Theorem to Identify Congruent Triangles

The Side-Side-Side (SSS) Congruence Theorem states that if three sides of one triangle are congruent to the corresponding sides of another triangle, then the triangles are congruent.

Example

According to the SSS Congruence Theorem, $\triangle MNP \cong \triangle XYZ$ because $\overline{MN} \cong \overline{XY}$, $\overline{NP} \cong \overline{YZ}$, and $\overline{MP} \cong \overline{XZ}$.

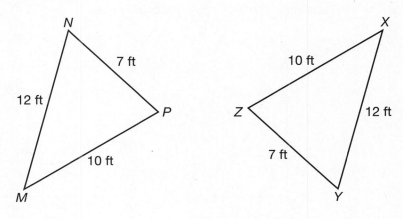

8.3

Using the SAS Congruence Theorem to Identify Congruent Triangle

The Side-Angle-Side (SAS) Congruence Theorem states that if two sides and the included angle of one triangle are congruent to the corresponding two sides and the included angle of a second triangle, then the triangles are congruent. An included angle is the angle formed by two sides of a triangle.

Example

According to the SAS Congruence Theorem, $\triangle ABC \cong \triangle HGF$ because $\overline{AB} \cong \overline{HG}$, $\overline{BC} \cong \overline{GF}$, and their corresponding included angles, $\angle B$ and $\angle G$, are congruent.

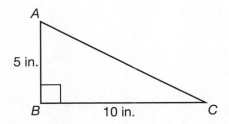
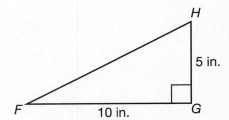

8.4 Using the ASA Congruence Theorem to Identify Congruent Triangles

The Angle-Side-Angle (ASA) Congruence Theorem states that if two angles and the included side of one triangle are congruent to the corresponding two angles and the included side of another triangle, then the triangles are congruent. An included side is the line segment between two angles of a triangle.

Example

According to the ASA Congruence Theorem, $\triangle RST \cong \triangle XYW$ because $\angle S \cong \angle Y$, $\angle T \cong \angle W$, and their corresponding included sides, $\overline{ST}$ and $\overline{WY}$, are congruent.

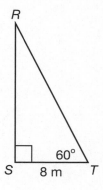
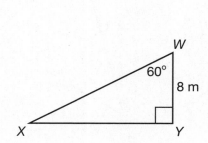

8.4 Using the AAS Congruence Theorem to Identify Congruent Triangles

The Angle-Angle-Side (AAS) Congruence Theorem states that if two angles and the non-included side of one triangle are congruent to the corresponding two angles and the non-included side of a second triangle, then the triangles are congruent.

Example

According to the AAS Congruence Theorem, $\triangle ABC \cong \triangle RPQ$ because $\angle A \cong \angle R$, $\angle B \cong \angle P$, and their corresponding non-included sides, $\overline{AC}$ and $\overline{RQ}$, are congruent.

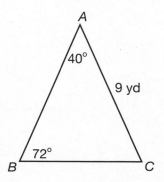
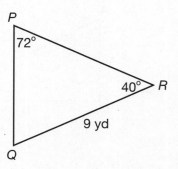

9 SIMILARITY

The pupils of a cat's eyes are shaped differently from ours. In brighter light, they appear narrow, like a diamond. But cat's eyes dilate just like ours do.

9

EXPANDING YOUR MIND

9.1

Dilations of Triangles

Learning Goals

In this lesson, you will:

► Dilate triangles that result in an enlargement of the original triangle.

► Dilate triangles that result in a reduction of the original triangle.

► Dilate triangles in a coordinate plane.

Key Terms

► dilation
► center of dilation
► scale factor
► dilation factor
► enlargement
► reduction

What does it mean if someone says that the pupils of your eyes are dilated? When a light source changes, the pupils of your eyes either shrink or enlarge to control the passage of light. When it is very sunny outside, your pupils will shrink to allow less light in. When it is very dark at night, your pupils will enlarge to allow more light in.

A change in light isn't the only thing that makes your pupils dilate. Your pupils can also enlarge when your eyes look at something you like: a favorite show, a cute animal, an interesting picture, or even a special someone.

Can you make your fellow pupils' pupils dilate? Try it out in your groups.

Problem 1   Maintaining Ratios–Enlargements

In mathematics, **dilations** are transformations that produce images that are the same shape as the original image, but not the same size. Each point on the original figure is moved along a straight line and the straight line is drawn from a fixed point known as the **center of dilation**. The distance each point moves is determined by the scale factor used.

The **scale factor** or **dilation factor** is the ratio of the distance of the image from the center of dilation to the distance of the original figure from the center of dilation.

When the scale factor is greater than one, the image is called an **enlargement**.

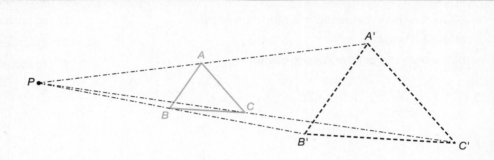

Triangle *ABC* was dilated to produce triangle *A'B'C'* using point *P* as the center of dilation. Triangle *A'B'C'* is an enlargement of triangle *ABC*.

Therefore, the scale factor can be expressed as $\frac{PA'}{PA} = \frac{PB'}{PB} = \frac{PC'}{PC}$.

1. How is the ratio *distance of the image from the center of dilation : distance of the original figure from the center of dilation* represented? Is the scale factor less than 1, equal to 1, or greater than 1? Explain your reasoning.

2. Measure each side of triangle *ABC* in millimeters.

   m$\overline{AB}$ = _____

   m$\overline{BC}$ = _____

   m$\overline{AC}$ = _____

3. Measure each side of triangle $A'B'C'$ in millimeters.

You will need a ruler and a protractor.

$m\overline{A'B'} =$ _____

$m\overline{B'C'} =$ _____

$m\overline{A'C'} =$ _____

4. Measure each line segment.

$m\overline{A'P} =$ _____mm $m\overline{AP} =$ _____mm

$m\overline{B'P} =$ _____mm $m\overline{BP} =$ _____mm

$m\overline{C'P} =$ _____mm $m\overline{CP} =$ _____mm

5. Determine each ratio.

$\dfrac{A'P}{AP} =$ _____ $\dfrac{B'P}{BP} =$ _____

$\dfrac{C'P}{CP} =$ _____ $\dfrac{A'B'}{AB} =$ _____

$\dfrac{B'C'}{BC} =$ _____ $\dfrac{A'C}{AC} =$ _____

6. Measure each angle in triangle ABC.

$m\angle A =$ _____°

$m\angle B =$ _____°

$m\angle C =$ _____°

7. Measure each angle in triangle $A'B'C'$.

Can I now add markers on triangles ABC and $A'B'C'$?

$m\angle A' =$ _____°

$m\angle B' =$ _____°

$m\angle C' =$ _____°

8. Compare triangle $A'B'C'$ to triangle ABC. What do you notice?

Problem 2 Maintaining Ratios—Reductions

When the scale factor or dilation factor is less than one, the image is called a **reduction**.

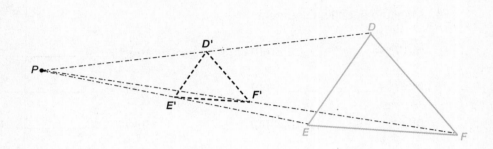

Triangle *DEF* was dilated to produce triangle *D'E'F'* using point *P* as the center of dilation. Triangle *D'E'F'* is a reduction of triangle *DEF*.

Therefore, the scale factor can be expressed as $\frac{PD'}{PD} = \frac{PE'}{PE} = \frac{PF'}{PF}$.

1. How is the ratio *distance of the image from the center of dilation : distance of the original figure from the center of dilation* represented? Is the scale factor less than 1, equal to 1, or greater than 1? Explain your reasoning.

2. Measure each side of triangle *DEF* in millimeters.

   m$\overline{DE}$ = _____

   m$\overline{EF}$ = _____

   m$\overline{DF}$ = _____

3. Measure each side of triangle *D'E'F'* in millimeters.

   m$\overline{D'E'}$ = _____

   m$\overline{E'F'}$ = _____

   m$\overline{D'F'}$ = _____

4. Measure each line segment.

$m\overline{D'P} =$ _____ mm $m\overline{DP} =$ _____ mm

$m\overline{E'P} =$ _____ mm $m\overline{EP} =$ _____ mm

$m\overline{F'P} =$ _____ mm $m\overline{FP} =$ _____ mm

5. Determine each ratio.

$\dfrac{D'P}{DP} =$ _____ $\dfrac{E'P}{EP} =$ _____

$\dfrac{F'P}{FP} =$ _____ $\dfrac{D'E'}{DE} =$ _____

$\dfrac{E'F'}{EF} =$ _____ $\dfrac{D'F}{DF} =$ _____

6. Measure each angle in triangle *DEF*.

$m\angle D =$ _____ °

$m\angle E =$ _____ °

$m\angle F =$ _____ °

How do these dilation ratios compare to the dilation ratios from Problem 1?

7. Measure each angle in triangle *D'E'F'*.

$m\angle D' =$ _____ °

$m\angle E' =$ _____ °

$m\angle F' =$ _____ °

8. Compare triangle *D'E'F'* to triangle *DEF*. What do you notice?

Can I add markers on triangles *DEF* and *D'E'F'*?

Problem 3   Dilating Triangles on a Coordinate Plane

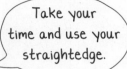

1. Enlarge triangle *WXY* with *P* as the center of dilation and a scale factor of 2. Follow the steps given.

Take your time and use your straightedge.

Step 1: Measure $\overline{PW}$, $\overline{PX}$, and $\overline{PY}$ in millimeters.

$m\overline{PW} = $ _____

$m\overline{PX} = $ _____

$m\overline{PY} = $ _____

Step 2:

- Extend line segment *PW* to point *W'* such that $m\overline{PW'} = 2 \times m\overline{PW}$.

- Extend line segment *PX* to point *X'* such that $m\overline{PX'} = 2 \times m\overline{PX}$.

- Extend line segment *PY* to point *Y'* such that $m\overline{PY'} = 2 \times m\overline{PY}$.

Step 3: Join points *W'*, *X'*, and *Y'* to form triangle *W'X'Y'*.

How can you verify triangle *W'X'Y'* was enlarged correctly?

2. Analyze triangle *ABC*.

    a. Dilate triangle *ABC* on the coordinate plane using the origin (0, 0) as the center of dilation and a scale factor of 2 to form triangle *A'B'C'*.

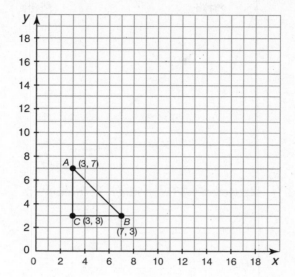

    b. What are the coordinates of points *A'*, *B'*, and *C'*?

3. Graph triangle *ABC* with the coordinates *A*(3, 7), *B*(7, 3), and *C*(3, 3) on the grid provided.

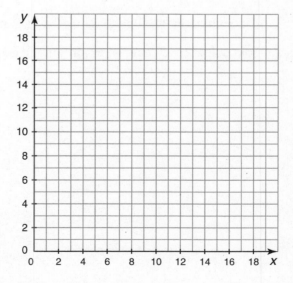

    a. Dilate triangle *ABC* on the coordinate plane using point *C* as the center of dilation and a scale factor of 3 to form triangle *A'B'C*.

    b. What are the coordinates of points *A'* and *B'*?

4. Reduce triangle *HJK* with *P* as the center of dilation and a scale factor of $\frac{1}{2}$. Follow the steps given.

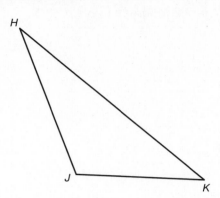

Step 1: Measure $\overline{PH}$, $\overline{PJ}$, and $\overline{PK}$ in millimeters.

$m\overline{PH} = $ _____

$m\overline{PJ} = $ _____

$m\overline{PK} = $ _____

Step 2:

- Locate point *H′* such that $m\overline{PH'} = \frac{1}{2} \times m\overline{PH}$.

- Locate point *J′* such that $m\overline{PJ'} = \frac{1}{2} \times m\overline{PJ}$.

- Locate point *K′* such that $m\overline{PK'} = \frac{1}{2} \times m\overline{PK}$.

Step 3: Join points *H′*, *J′*, and *K′* to form triangle *H′J′K′*.

How can you verify that triangle *H′J′K′* was reduced correctly?

5. Analyze triangle *ABC*.

a. Dilate triangle *ABC* on the coordinate plane using the origin (0, 0) as the center of dilation and a scale factor of $\frac{1}{2}$ to form triangle *A'B'C'*.

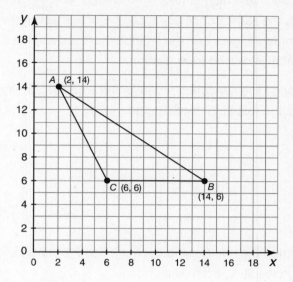

b. What are the coordinates of points *A'*, *B'*, and *C'*?

6. Graph triangle *ABC* with the coordinates *A*(3, 15), *B*(15, 3), and *C*(3, 3) on the grid provided.

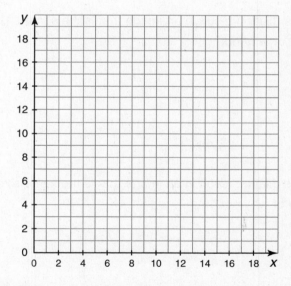

a. Dilate triangle *ABC* on the coordinate plane using point *C* as the center of dilation and a scale factor of $\frac{1}{2}$ to form triangle *A'B'C*.

b. What are the coordinates of points *A'* and *B'*?

Talk the Talk

In this lesson, several triangles were dilated. Whether it was an enlargement or a reduction, the same conclusions can be drawn about the relationship between corresponding angles and the relationship between the corresponding sides of a triangle and its image resulting from dilation.

1. Describe the relationship between the corresponding angles in an original triangle and its image resulting from dilation.

2. Describe the relationship between the corresponding sides in an original figure and its image resulting from dilation.

3. Does dilation result in an image that is the same shape as the original? Why or why not?

4. Does dilation result in an image that is the same size as the original? Why or why not?

5. If two triangles are congruent, what is the relationship between the corresponding angles?

6. If two triangles are congruent, what is the relationship between the corresponding sides?

7. Describe how a triangle is dilated when the ratio *distance of the image from the center of dilation : distance of the original figure from the center of dilation* is:

- less than 1.

- equal to 1.

- greater than 1.

Be prepared to share your solutions and methods.

9

LOOK-ALIKES
Similar Triangles

9.2

9

Learning Goals

In this lesson, you will:

▶ Define similar triangles.

▶ Identify the corresponding parts of similar triangles.

▶ Write triangle similarity statements.

▶ Determine the measure of corresponding parts of similar triangles.

Key Term

▶ similar triangles

Turquoise, navy, cobalt, robin's egg, cornflower, ultramarine, aquamarine, cerulean, and periwinkle—all of these are names for different shades of the color blue. There are an infinite number of possibilities for shades of blue, but all of them are similar in one way: They are all blue.

What are some examples of similarity you have learned in mathematics?

Problem 1   Similar Triangles

Similar triangles are triangles that have the same shape.

In the previous lesson, you learned that when a triangle is dilated, the resulting image is an enlarged or reduced triangle that maintains the same shape as the original triangle. Dilations resulted in congruent corresponding angles, and proportional corresponding sides based on the scale factor or dilation ratio.

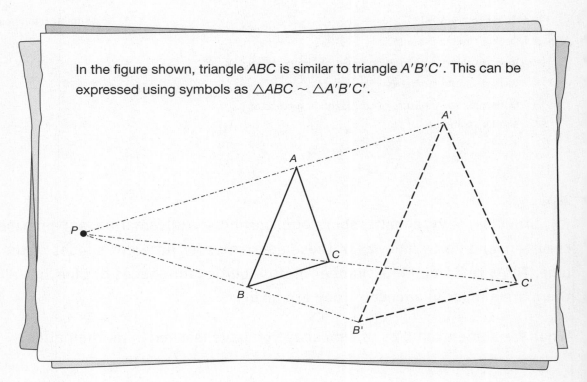

In the figure shown, triangle *ABC* is similar to triangle *A'B'C'*. This can be expressed using symbols as △*ABC* ~ △*A'B'C'*.

1. Use the figure shown to answer each question.

   a. Identify the congruent corresponding angles.

   b. Write ratios to identify the proportional sides.

2. Given $\triangle TRP \sim \triangle WMY$:

    a. Identify the congruent corresponding angles.

    b. Write ratios to identify the proportional sides.

3. Suppose $\angle K \cong \angle H$, $\angle P \cong \angle O$, $\angle E \cong \angle W$, and $\dfrac{KP}{HO} = \dfrac{PE}{OW} = \dfrac{KE}{HW}$.
Write a triangle similarity statement.

1. Given: △*ZAP* ~ △*EDP*

   PZ = 5 cm, *ZA* = 4 cm, and *ED* = 12 cm

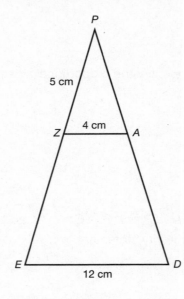

Think about the similar triangles given. What does this tell you?

a. What other measurement(s) can you determine? Explain how you know.

b. Determine the measurement(s).

2. Given: △ZAP ~ △EDP

m∠E = 47°

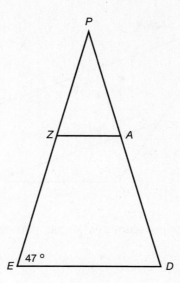

a. What other measurement(s) can you determine? Explain how you know.

b. Determine the measurement(s).

3. Given: $\triangle WRM \sim \triangle WGQ$

$WQ = 5$ cm, $WG = 6$ cm, and $GR = 8$ cm

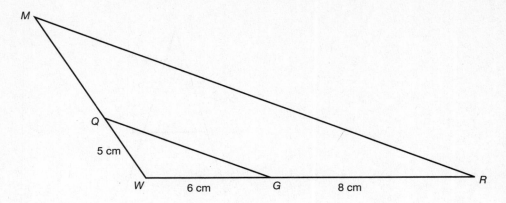

a. What other measurement(s) can you determine? Explain how you know.

b. Determine the measurement(s).

4. Given: $\triangle DFH \sim \triangle TKH$

TK = 5.5 ft, KH = 6 ft, and FK = 15 ft

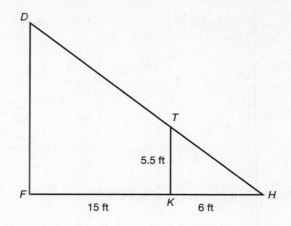

a. What other measurement(s) can you determine? Explain how you know.

b. Determine the measurement(s).

5. Given: $\triangle WBE \sim \triangle SEP$

   $BP = EP, WE = 58$ mm

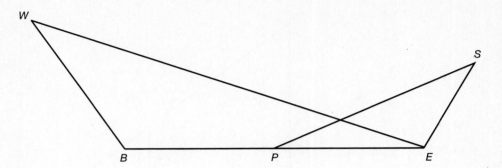

a. What other measurement(s) can you determine? Explain how you know.

b. Determine the measurement(s).

Be prepared to share your solutions and methods.

PROVE IT!

AA, SAS, and SSS Similarity Theorems

Learning Goals

In this lesson, you will:

▶ Explore the AA Similarity Theorem.

▶ Explore the SAS Similarity Theorem.

▶ Explore the SSS Similarity Theorem.

▶ Use the AA, SAS, and SSS Similarity Theorems to identify similar triangles.

Key Terms

▶ AA Similarity Theorem

▶ SAS Similarity Theorem

▶ SSS Similarity Theorem

Graphic artists often use knowledge about similarity to create realistic-looking perspective drawings. Choose where the horizon should be and a vanishing point—a point where all parallel lines in the drawing should appear to meet—and you too can create a perspective drawing.

Can you see how similarity was used to create this drawing? Can you use similarity to create your own perspective drawing?

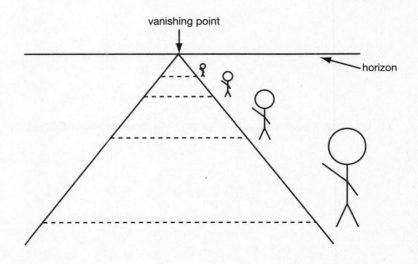

Problem 1   Two Angles

In the previous lesson, you determined that when two triangles are similar, the corresponding angles are congruent and the corresponding sides are proportional. To show that two triangles are similar, do you need to show that all of the corresponding sides are proportional and all of the corresponding angles are congruent? In this lesson, you will explore efficient methods for showing that two triangles are similar.

1. If the measures of two angles of a triangle are known, is that enough information to draw a similar triangle? Let's explore this possibility.

   a. Use a straightedge to draw triangle *ABC* in the space provided.

   b. Use a protractor to measure, ∠*A* and ∠*B*, of triangle *ABC* and record the measurements.

      m∠*A* = _____   m∠*B* = _____

   c. Do you need a protractor to determine m∠*C*? Why or why not?

Do you remember what the sum of the angle measures in a triangle is?

   d. Use the measurements in part (b) to draw triangle *DEF* in the space provided.

e. Based on your knowledge from the previous lesson, what other information is needed to determine if the two triangles are similar and how can you acquire that information?

f. Determine the measurements to get the additional information needed and decide if the two triangles are similar.

You have just shown that given the measures of two pairs of congruent corresponding angles of two triangles, it is possible to determine that two triangles are similar. In the study of geometry, this is expressed as a theorem.

The **Angle-Angle (AA) Similarity Theorem** states that if two angles of one triangle are congruent to the corresponding angles of another triangle, then the triangles are similar.

2. Analyze triangle *ABC*.

   a. Dilate triangle *ABC* on the coordinate plane using the origin (0, 0) as the center of dilation and a scale factor of 3 to form triangle *A'B'C'*.

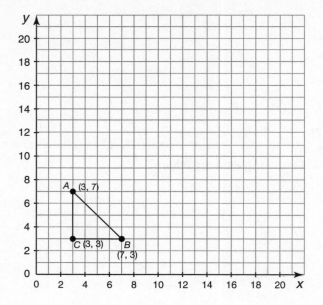

   b. What are the coordinates of points *A'*, *B'*, and *C'*?

   c. Use the AA Similarity Theorem and a protractor to determine if the original triangle, △*ABC*, and the image resulting from the dilation, △*A'B'C'*, are similar triangles.

If the center of dilation is at the origin, can that help you determine the coordinates of *A'*, *B'*, and *C'*?

Problem 2   Two Sides and the Included Angle

If the lengths of two sides and the measure of the included angle of a triangle are known, is that enough information to draw a similar triangle?

1. Let's explore this possibility.

    a. Use a straightedge to draw triangle *ABC* in the space provided.

> Remember, you explored a *similar* situation when analyzing congruent triangles.

    b. Use a ruler to measure the lengths of $\overline{AB}$ and $\overline{BC}$, of triangle *ABC* and record the measurements.

        m$\overline{AB}$ = _____   m$\overline{BC}$ = _____

    c. Use a protractor to measure ∠*B*, the included angle in triangle *ABC*, and record the measurement.

        m∠*B* = _____

    d. Use the measurements in parts (b) to draw two sides of a triangle that are proportional to the corresponding sides of triangle *ABC*, and use the angle measure in part (c) to draw an included angle that is congruent, in order to form triangle *DEF* in the space provided.

e. Based on your knowledge from the previous lesson, what other information is needed to determine if the two triangles are similar and how can you acquire that information?

f. Determine the measurements to get the additional information needed and decide if the two triangles are similar.

You have just shown that given the lengths of two sides of a triangle and the measure of the included angle, it is possible to determine that two triangles are similar. In the study of geometry, this is expressed as a theorem.

The **Side-Angle-Side (SAS) Similarity Theorem** states that if two pairs of corresponding sides of two triangles are proportional and the included angles are congruent, then the triangles are similar.

2. Use the SAS Similarity Theorem and a protractor to determine if the two triangles drawn on the coordinate plane are similar. Use a protractor to verify the measure of the included angle.

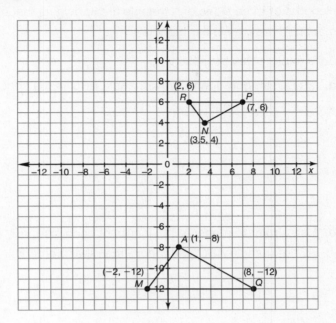

Problem 3   Three Sides

If the lengths of three sides of a triangle are known, is that enough information to draw a similar triangle?

Remember, you explored a *similar* situation with congruent triangles.

1. Let's explore this possibility.

   a. Use a straightedge to draw triangle *ABC* in the space provided.

   b. Use a ruler to measure the length of each side, *AB, BC,* and *AC,* of triangle *ABC* and record the measurements.

   $m\overline{AB} =$ _____ $m\overline{BC} =$ _____ $m\overline{AC} =$ _____

   c. Use the measurements in parts (b) to draw three sides of a triangle that are proportional to these measurements to form triangle *DEF* in the space provided.

   d. Michael says that based on what he's learned so far, he needs to find the measures of the three corresponding angles of the triangles to determine if they are similar. Is he correct? Why or why not?

   e. Determine the measurements to get the additional information needed and decide if the two triangles are similar.

You have just shown that given the length of three sides of a triangle, it is possible to determine that two triangles are similar. In the study of geometry, this method is expressed as a theorem.

The **Side-Side-Side (SSS) Similarity Theorem** states that if three pairs of corresponding sides of two triangles are proportional, then the triangles are similar.

2. Use the SSS Similarity Theorem to determine if the two triangles drawn on the coordinate plane are similar.

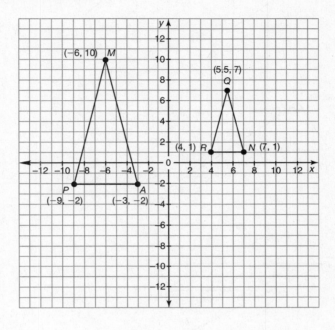

Talk the Talk

Determine if each pair of triangles are similar by AA, SAS, or SSS.

1.

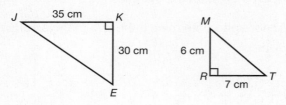

2.

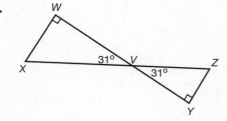

3.

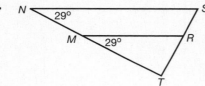

4.

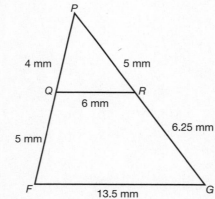

Be prepared to share your solutions and methods.

BACK ON THE GRID
Similar Triangles on the Coordinate Plane

9.4

9

Learning Goals

In this lesson, you will:

▶ Graph similar triangles and determine the dilation factor.

▶ Dilate triangles to form similar triangles.

▶ Verify that triangles are similar using Similarity Theorems.

▶ Determine the coordinates of a point needed to form similar triangles.

You know that the Earth is farther away from the Sun than the planet Venus. But is there a way to tell just by looking? Amazingly, the ancient Greeks used similar triangles to figure this out.

They observed that Venus was never more than 47° high in the sky at sunset.

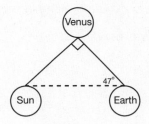

And they knew something that you will learn later in mathematics—that for any angle in a right triangle, the ratio of the opposite side length to the hypotenuse is always the same for all similar triangles, no matter what these lengths are.

The ancient Greeks knew that for a 47° angle, the ratio of the opposite side to the hypotenuse was about 0.72. This meant that the Venus-Sun distance was about $\frac{7}{10}$ of the Earth-Sun distance. Venus is closer!

Can you see how they did it?

Problem 1 Similar Triangles Resulting from Dilations

Let's explore methods for showing two triangles are similar through dilations.

1. Triangle *ABC* has vertices *A*(3, −3), *B*(8, 3), and *C*(8, −3).

   a. Graph triangle *ABC*.

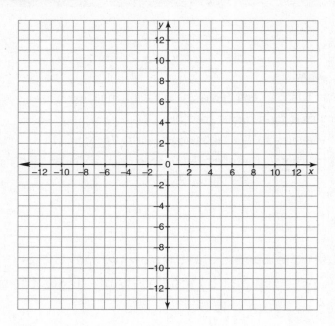

   b. Triangle *DEF* is the image that resulted from the dilation of triangle *ABC*. The coordinates of triangle *DEF* are *D* (1.5, −1.5), *E* (4, 1.5), and *F* (4, −1.5). Graph triangle *DEF* on the coordinate plane in part (a).

   c. What scale factor was used?

   d. How did you determine the scale factor?

   e. Is the dilation an enlargement or reduction? Explain your reasoning.

f. How can you verify that triangle *ABC* and triangle *DEF* are similar?

g. Use the SAS Similarity Theorem to verify triangle *ABC* is similar to triangle *DEF*.

2. Triangle *MAP* is the image that resulted from the dilation of triangle *QRN*.

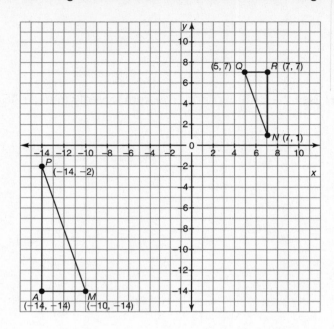

a. What scale factor was used?

b. How did you determine the scale factor?

c. Is the dilation an enlargement or reduction? Explain your reasoning.

d. How can you verify that triangle *MAP* and triangle *QRN* are similar?

e. Use the SSS Similarity Theorem to verify triangle *MAP* is similar to triangle *QRN*.

3. Analyze triangle *PWN*.

   a. Dilate triangle *PWN* shown using a scale factor of 4 to form triangle *GKA*.

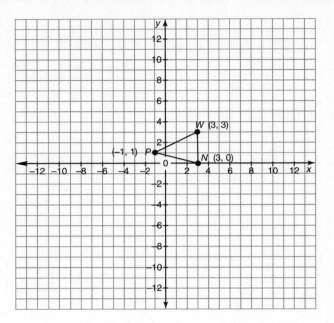

   b. What are the coordinates of the dilated image?

   c. How did you determine the coordinates of the dilated image?

   d. Is the dilation an enlargement or reduction? Explain your reasoning.

   e. How can you verify that triangle *PWN* and triangle *GKA* are similar?

   f. Use the AA Similarity Theorem to verify triangle *PWN* is similar to triangle *GKA*.

4. Analyze triangle *ZEN*.

    a. Dilate triangle *ZEN* shown using a scale factor of $\frac{1}{2}$ to form triangle *FRB*.

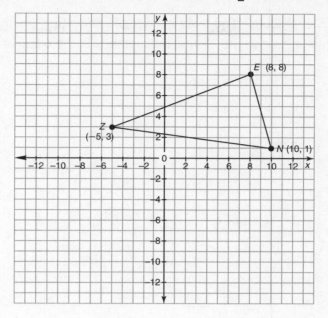

    b. What are the coordinates of the dilated image?

    c. How did you determine the coordinates of the dilated image?

    d. Is the dilation an enlargement or reduction? Explain your reasoning.

    e. Use the AA Similarity Theorem to verify triangle *ZEN* is similar to triangle *FRB*.

Talk the Talk

This chapter focused on three methods to show that two triangles are similar. Complete the graphic organizer by listing the methods and provide an illustration of each method.

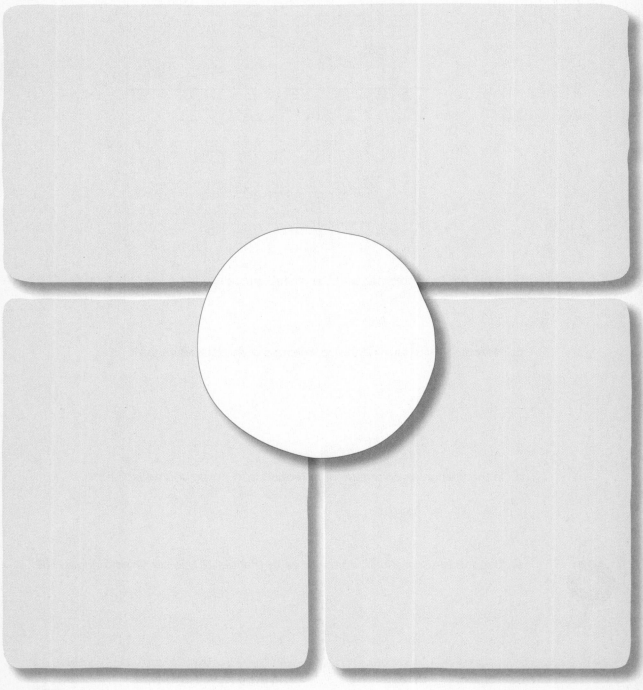

Be prepared to share your solutions and methods.

Key Terms

▶ dilation (9.1)
▶ center of dilation (9.1)
▶ scale factor (9.1)
▶ dilation factor (9.1)
▶ enlargement (9.1)

▶ reduction (9.1)
▶ similar triangles (9.2)
▶ AA Similarity Theorem (9.3)
▶ SAS Similarity Theorem (9.3)
▶ SSS Similarity Theorem (9.3)

9

9.1 Dilating Triangles

Dilations are transformations that produce images that are the same shape as the original image, but not the same size. Each point on the original figure is moved along a straight line and the straight line is drawn from a fixed point known as the center of dilation. The scale factor is the ratio formed when comparing the distance of the image from the center of dilation to the distance of the original figure from the center of dilation.

Example

Enlarge triangle ABC with P as the center of dilation and a scale factor of 2.

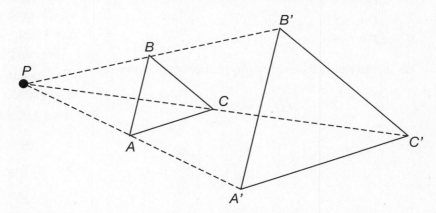

First, measure PA. Then, extend the line PA to the point A' such that $PA' = 2PA$.

Next, measure PB. Then, extend the line PB to the point B' such that $PB' = 2PB$.

Finally, measure PC. Then, extend the line PC to the point C' such that $PC' = 2PC$.

Because the scale factor is greater than one, the image $A'B'C'$ is called an enlargement. If the scale factor had been less than one, the image would be called a reduction.

9.2 Properties of Similar Triangles

Similar triangles are triangles that have the same shape.

Example

In the figure shown, triangle *DEF* is similar to triangle *D'E'F'*. This can be expressed using symbols as △*DEF* ~ △*D'E'F'*.

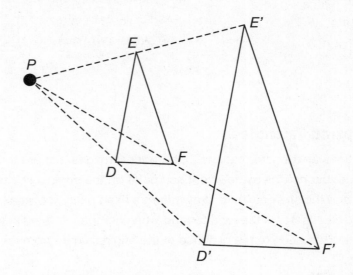

1. Identify the congruent corresponding angles.

   $\angle D \cong \angle D'$

   $\angle E \cong \angle E'$

   $\angle F \cong \angle F'$

2. Write ratios to identify the proportional sides.

   $\dfrac{D'E'}{DE} = \dfrac{E'F'}{EF} = \dfrac{F'D'}{FD}$

I am going to be an architect and they use these skills all the time. Understanding this already will be a big help when it comes time to go to college.

9.2 Using Similar Triangles to Find Unknown Measures

The properties of similar triangles can be used to determine unknown measures of the triangles.

Example

In the figure shown, triangle *ACE* is similar to triangle *BCD*. Find the length of side *AC*.

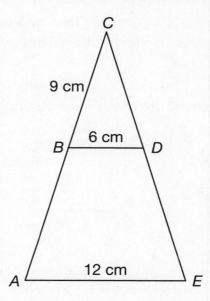

Using the proportional relationship between corresponding sides of similar triangles, you know $\frac{BC}{AC} = \frac{BD}{AE}$.

Substitute the known values for the sides.

$$\frac{BC}{AC} = \frac{BD}{AE}$$

$$\frac{9}{AC} = \frac{6}{12}$$

$6AC = (9)(12)$

$6AC = 108$

$AC = 18$

The length of side *AC* is 18 centimeters.

AA, SAS, and SSS Similarity Theorems

The Angle-Angle (AA) Similarity Theorem states: "If two angles of one triangle are congruent to the corresponding angles of another triangle, then the triangles are similar."

The Side-Angle-Side (SAS) Similarity Theorem states: "If two pairs of corresponding sides of two triangles are proportional and the included angles are congruent, then the triangles are similar."

The Side-Side-Side (SSS) Similarity Theorem states: "If three pairs of corresponding sides of two triangles are proportional, then the triangles are similar."

Example

Determine if each pair of triangles are similar by AA, SAS, or SSS.

1.

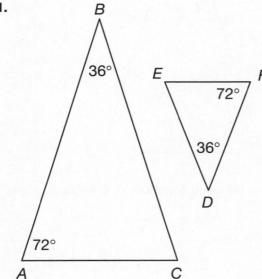

$\angle A = \angle F$

$\angle B = \angle D$

$\triangle ABC \sim \triangle FDE$

The triangles are similar by AA.

2.

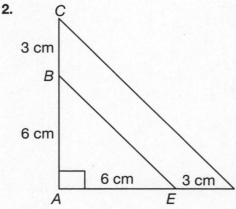

$\dfrac{AB}{AC} = \dfrac{AE}{AD}$

$\dfrac{6}{9} = \dfrac{6}{9}$

$\angle A = \angle A$

$\triangle ABE \sim \triangle ACD$

The triangles are similar by SAS.

3.

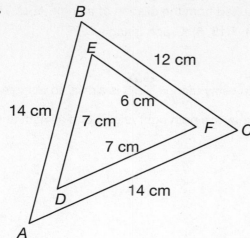

$$\frac{AB}{DE} = \frac{14}{7} \qquad\qquad \frac{BC}{EF} = \frac{12}{6}$$

$$= \frac{2}{1} \qquad\qquad\qquad = \frac{2}{1}$$

$$\frac{CA}{FD} = \frac{14}{7}$$

$$= \frac{2}{1}$$

$$\frac{AB}{DE} = \frac{BC}{EF} = \frac{CA}{FD}$$

$$\frac{2}{1} = \frac{2}{1} = \frac{2}{1}$$

$$\triangle ABC \sim \triangle DEF$$

The triangles are similar by SSS.

9.4 Similar Triangles on the Coordinate Plane

Properties of similar triangles can be used to graph similar triangles, determine the scale factor that was used to create the triangles, and verify that the triangles are similar.

Example

Triangle ABC has vertices $A(1,2)$, $B(1, 5)$, $C(5, 2)$. Graph triangle ABC.

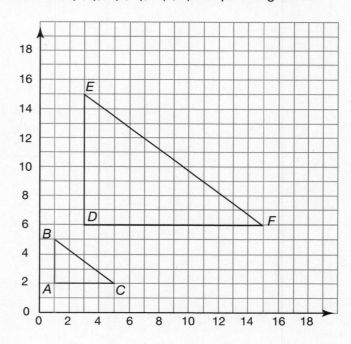

Triangle *DEF* is the image that resulted from the dilation of triangle *ABC*. The coordinates of triangle *DEF* are *D*(3,6), *E*(3, 15), *F*(15, 6). Graph triangle *DEF*.

The scale factor used was 3.

Use the SAS Similarity Theorem to verify triangle *ABC* is similar to triangle *DEF*.

∠*A* is congruent to ∠*D* because they are both right angles and all right angles are congruent.

$$\frac{AB}{DE} = \frac{AC}{DF}$$

$$\frac{3}{9} = \frac{4}{12}$$

$$\frac{1}{3} = \frac{1}{3}$$

The lengths of the sides that include ∠*A* and ∠*D* are proportional.

Triangle *ABC* is similar to triangle *DEF* by the SAS Similarity Theorem.

GLOSSARY

---A---

absolute value function

An absolute value function is a function that can be written in the form $f(x) = |x|$ where x is any number.

Additive Identity

The number 0 is the additive identity because when 0 is added to any number, the sum is that number.

Examples

$0 + 65 = 65$ $\qquad\qquad$ $p + 0 = p$

Additive Inverse

Two numbers are additive inverses if their sum is the additive identity, or 0.

Examples

$a + -a = 0$ $\qquad\qquad$ $-19 + 19 = 0$

adjacent angles

Adjacent angles are two angles that share a common vertex and share a common side.

Example

Angles BAC and CAD are <u>adjacent angles.</u> The angles share the vertex A and the side AC.

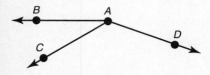

alternate exterior angles

Alternate exterior angles are angles formed when a line (transversal) intersects two other lines. These angles are on opposite sides of the transversal and are outside the other two lines.

Example

Angles 1 and 2 are <u>alternate exterior angles.</u>

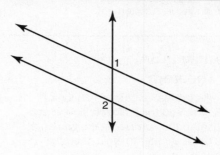

alternate interior angles

Alternate interior angles are angles formed when a line (transversal) intersects two other lines. These angles are on opposite sides of the transversal and are between the other two lines.

Example

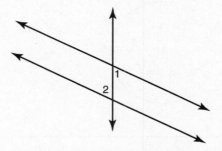

Angles 1 and 2 are <u>alternate interior angles.</u>

angle of rotation

The <u>angle of rotation</u> is the amount of rotation, in degrees, about a fixed point.

Angle-Angle (AA) Similarity Theorem

The Angle-Angle (AA) Similarity Theorem states that if two angles of one triangle are congruent to the corresponding angles of another triangle, then the triangles are similar.

Angle-Angle-Side (AAS) Congruence Theorem

The Angle-Angle-Side (AAS) Congruence Theorem states that if two angles and a non-included side of one triangle are congruent to the corresponding angles and the corresponding non-included side of a second triangle, then the triangles are congruent.

Angle-Side-Angle (ASA) Congruence Theorem

The Angle-Side-Angle (ASA) Congruence Theorem states that if two angles and the included side of one triangle are congruent to the corresponding two angles and the included side of another triangle, then the triangles are congruent.

antipodes

The antipodes of a sphere are the endpoints of a diameter.

Example

Points A and B are the <u>antipodes</u> of the sphere shown.

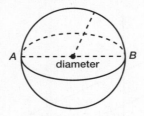

associations

The patterns or relationships identified in scatter plots of a two-variable data set are called associations.

Associative Property of Addition

The Associative Property of Addition states that changing the grouping of the terms in an addition problem does not change the sum. For any numbers a, b, and c, $(a + b) + c = a + (b + c)$.

Examples

$$4 + (3 + 2) = (4 + 3) + 2$$

$$4 + 5 = 7 + 2$$
$$9 = 9$$

$$(2x + 5x) + 5x = 2x + (5x + 5x)$$

$$7x + 5x = 2x + 10x$$
$$12x = 12x$$

Associative Property of Multiplication

The Associative Property of Multiplication states that changing the grouping of the terms in a multiplication problem does not change the product. For any numbers a, b, and c, $(a \times b) \times c = a \times (b \times c)$

Examples

$$(12 \times 5) \times 2 = 12 \times (5 \times 2)$$

$$60 \times 2 = 12 \times 10$$
$$120 = 120$$

$$\frac{1}{5} \cdot \left(\frac{1}{3} \cdot \frac{1}{2}\right) = \left(\frac{1}{5} \cdot \frac{1}{3}\right) \cdot \frac{1}{2}$$

$$\frac{1}{5} \cdot \frac{1}{6} = \frac{1}{15} \cdot \frac{1}{2}$$

$$\frac{1}{30} = \frac{1}{30}$$

———— B ————

base

The base of a power is the expression that is used as a factor in the repeated multiplication.

Examples

$$2^3 = 2 \times 2 \times 2 = 8 \qquad 8^0 = 1$$

<u>base</u> <u>base</u>

break-even point

When one line represents the cost of an item and the other line represents the income from selling the item, the point of intersection is also called the break-even point.

C

categorical data

Categorical data are data that each fit into exactly one of several different groups, or categories. Categorical data are also called "qualitative data."

Examples

Animals: lions, tigers, bears, etc.
U.S. Cities: Los Angeles, Atlanta, New York City, Dodge City, etc.

---

center of a sphere

The center of a sphere is a fixed point in space that is at an equal distance from every point on the sphere.

Example

The <u>center</u> and radius of the sphere are labeled.

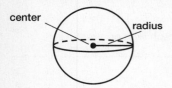

---

center of dilation

The point from which a dilation is generated is called the center of dilation.

Example

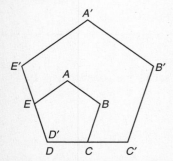

The <u>center of dilation</u> is point D.

characteristic

In an expression of the form $a \times 10^n$, the variable n is called the characteristic.

Example $6.1 \times 10^5 = 610,000$

<u>characteristic</u>

---

circumference

The distance around a circle or a cylinder is known as the circumference. The circumference is calculated by the following formula: $C = \pi(d)$.

---

closure

A set of numbers is said to be closed under an operation if the result of the operation on two numbers in the set is a defined value also in the set.

---

clustered

When the points on a scatter plot are clustered, the data values are arranged in such a way that as you look at the graph from left to right, you can imagine a line going through the scatter plot with most of the points being clustered close to the line.

---

coincidental lines

Coincidental lines are lines that have equivalent linear equations and overlap at every point when they are graphed.

Commutative Property of Addition

The Commutative Property of Addition states that changing the order of two or more terms in an addition problem does not change the sum. For any numbers a and b, $a + b = b + a$.

Examples

$$\begin{array}{r} 1 \\ + 2.102 \\ \hline 3.102 \end{array} = \begin{array}{r} 2.102 \\ + 1 \\ \hline 3.102 \end{array}$$

$$\underbrace{\frac{1}{9} + \frac{7}{9} + \frac{5}{9}}_{\frac{13}{9}} = \underbrace{\frac{7}{9} + \frac{5}{9} + \frac{1}{9}}_{\frac{13}{9}}$$

Commutative Property of Multiplication

The Commutative Property of Multiplication states that changing the order of two or more factors in a multiplication problem does not change the product. For any numbers a and b, $a \times b = b \times a$.

Examples

$$
\begin{array}{r}
7.2 \\
\times\ 0.59 \\
\hline
648 \\
+\ 3600 \\
\hline
4.248
\end{array}
\qquad
\begin{array}{r}
0.59 \\
\times\ 7.2 \\
\hline
118 \\
4130 \\
\hline
4.248
\end{array}
$$

$$\frac{1}{5} \times \frac{2}{3} \times \frac{3}{8} = \frac{2}{3} \times \frac{1}{5} \times \frac{3}{8}$$

$$\frac{6}{120} = \frac{1}{20} \qquad \frac{6}{120} = \frac{1}{20}$$

cone

A cone is a three-dimensional figure with a circular or elliptical base and one vertex.

congruent angles

Congruent angles are two or more angles that have equal measures.

congruent line segments

Line segments that have the same length are called congruent line segments.

consistent system

A system of equations that has one or many solutions is called a consistent system.

constant function

When the y-value does not change or remains constant, the function is called a constant function.

constant interval

When a function is constant for some values of the independent variable, it is said to have a constant interval.

continuous graph

A continuous graph is a graph with no breaks in it.

converse

The converse of a theorem is created when the if-then parts of that theorem are exchanged.

Example

Triangle Inequality Theorem:

If a polygon is a triangle, then the sum of any two of its side lengths is always greater than the length of the third side.

Converse of Triangle Inequality Theorem:

If you have three side lengths, and the sum of any two of the side lengths is greater than the third side length, then the side lengths can form a triangle.

Converse of the Pythagorean Theorem

The Converse of the Pythagorean Theorem states: If the lengths of the sides of a triangle satisfy the equation $a^2 + b^2 = c^2$, then the triangle is a right triangle.

Example

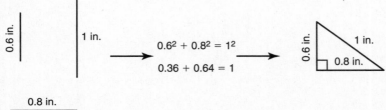

$$0.6^2 + 0.8^2 = 1^2$$
$$0.36 + 0.64 = 1$$

coplanar lines

Coplanar lines are two or more lines that are located in the same plane.

corresponding angles

Corresponding angles are angles that have the same relative positions in geometric figures

Example

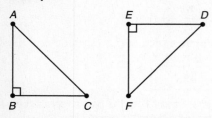

Angle B and Angle E are <u>corresponding angles</u>.

corresponding sides

Corresponding sides are sides that have the same relative positions in geometric figures.

Example

Sides AB and DE are <u>corresponding sides</u>.

cubic function

A cubic function is function that can be written in the form $f(x) = a_3x^3 + a_2x^2 + a_1x + a_0$.

cylinder

A cylinder is a three-dimensional object with two parallel, congruent, circular bases.

——— D ———

decreasing function

When the value of a dependent variable decreases as the independent variable increases, the function is said to be a decreasing function.

dependent system

A dependent system is a system of equations that has infinitely many solutions.

dependent variable (response variable)

The dependent variable is the variable whose value is determined by an independent variable. It can also be called the response variable because it is the variable that responds to what occurs to the explanatory variable.

diagonal of a square

A diagonal of a square is a line segment connecting opposite vertices of the square.

diameter of a sphere

A segment drawn between two points on the sphere that passes through the center is a diameter.

Example

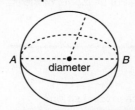

The <u>diameter of the sphere</u> is labeled.

dilation factor

The dilation factor is the ratio of the distance of the image from the center of dilation to the distance of the original figure from the center of dilation. This is also known as the scale factor.

dilations

Dilations are transformations that produce images that are the same shape as the original image, but not the same size.

Example

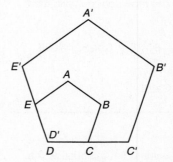

Pentagon $ABCDE$ has been dilated by a scale factor of 2 about point D to create pentagon $A'B'C'D'E'$.

direct variation

When a linear equation is written in y-intercept form, the variables x and y show direct variation. Direct variation is the relationship between two quantities x and y such that the two variables have a constant ratio.

Example

If Melissa earns $8.25 per hour, then the amount she earns is in <u>direct variation</u> with the number of hours she works. The amount $8.25 is a constant.

discrete graph

A discrete graph is a graph of isolated points.

domain

The domain of a function is the set of all inputs of the function.

---- **E** ----

ellipsis

An ellipsis is three periods that mean "and so on."

enlargement

When the scale factor is greater than one, the image is called an enlargement.

estimation

When you do not need to know the exact value of an expression, you can use estimation to determine the approximate value.

exponent

The exponent of a power is the number of times that the base is used as a factor in the repeated multiplication.

Examples

$2^3 = 2 \times 2 \times 2 = 8$ $8^4 = 8 \times 8 \times 8 \times 8 = 4096$

<u>exponent</u>   <u>exponent</u>

extrapolating

Extrapolating is predicting values that fall outside the plotted values on a scatter plot.

---- **F** ----

first differences

First differences are the values determined by subtracting consecutive y-values in a table when the x-values are consecutive integers. When the first differences are equal, the points represented by the ordered pairs in the table will form a straight line.

Example

x	y
1	25
2	34
3	45

 9

11

The <u>first differences</u> are 9 and 11, so the points represented by these ordered pairs will not form a straight line.

frequency

The frequency of a variable is the number of times it appears in a data set.

Example

Number Rolled	Tally	Frequency
2	JHI II	7

The number 2 was rolled 7 times, so its <u>frequency</u> was 7.

function

A function maps each input to one and only one output.

---- **G** ----

great circle

A great circle is the circumference of the sphere at the sphere's widest part.

Example

Point A is the center of the sphere. It is also the center of the <u>great circle</u>.

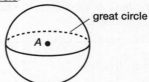

Glossary

height of a cone

The height of a cone is the length of a line segment drawn from the vertex to the base of the cone. The line segment is perpendicular to the base.

height of a cylinder

The height of a cylinder is the length of a line segment drawn from one base to the other base. This line segment is perpendicular to the other base.

hemisphere

A hemisphere is half of a sphere bounded by a great circle.

Example

A <u>hemisphere</u> is shown.

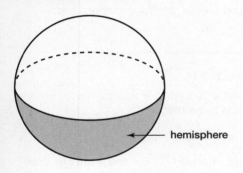

hemisphere

hypotenuse

The hypotenuse of a right triangle is the side opposite the right angle.

Examples

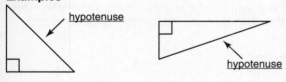

hypotenuse

hypotenuse

image

The new figure created from a transformation is called the image.

Example

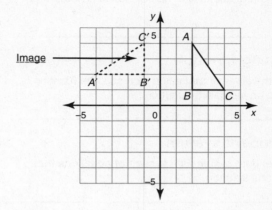

Image

included angle

An included angle is an angle formed by two consecutive sides of a figure.

Example

In triangle *ABC*, angle *A* is the <u>included angle</u> formed by consecutive sides $\overline{AB}$ and $\overline{AC}$.

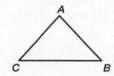

included side

An included side is a line segment between two consecutive angles of a figure.

Example

In triangle *ABC*, $\overline{AB}$ is the <u>included side</u> formed by consecutive angles *A* and *B*.

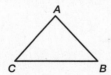

Glossary

income

Income is the amount of money earned from sales.

inconsistent systems

A system of equations with no solution is called an inconsistent system.

increasing function

When both values of a function increase, the function is said to be an increasing function.

independent system

An independent system is a system of equations that has only one solution.

independent variable (explanatory variable)

The independent variable, also called the explanatory variable, is the variable whose value is not determined by another variable.

input

The first coordinate of an ordered pair in a relation is the input.

interpolating

Interpolating is predicting values that will fall within the plotted values on a scatter plot.

intersecting lines

Intersecting lines are lines in a plane that intersect, or cross each other.

Example

interval of decrease

When a function is decreasing for some values of the independent variable, it is said to have an interval of decrease.

interval of increase

When a function is increasing for some values of the independent variable, it is said to have an interval of increase.

inverse operation

An inverse operation is an operation that undoes another operation.

Examples

Addition and subtraction are inverse operations:
$351 + 25 - 25 = 351$.

Multiplication and division are inverse operations:
$351 \times 25 \div 25 = 351$.

irrational number

An irrational number is a number that cannot be written as $\frac{a}{b}$, where a and b are integers.

Examples

The numbers $\sqrt{2}$, 0.313113111..., and π are irrational numbers.

—— **L** ——

leg

A leg of a right triangle is either of the two shorter sides. Together, the two legs form the right angle of a right triangle.

Examples

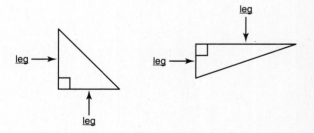

line of best fit

A line of best fit is a line that is as close to as many points as possible, but doesn't have to go through all the points.

Example

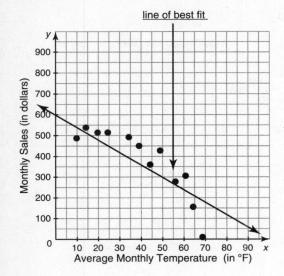

linear association

A linear association occurs when the points on the scatter plot seem to form a line.

Example

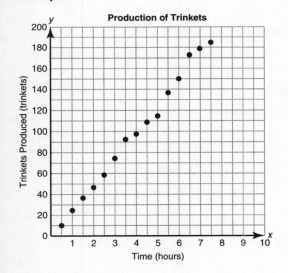

linear combinations method (elimination)

The linear combinations method is a process to solve a system of equations by adding two equations to each other, resulting in an equation with one variable.

linear function

A function whose graph is a straight line is a linear function.

Example

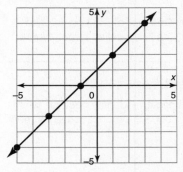

The function $f(x) = x + 1$ is a <u>linear function.</u>

linear graph

A linear graph is a graph that is a line or a series of collinear points.

linear pair of angles

A linear pair of angles, or a linear pair, consists of two adjacent angles that form a straight line.

Example

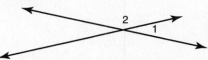

Angles 1 and 2 are a <u>linear pair</u>.

linear regression

Linear regression means to model the relationship of two variables in a data set by drawing a line of best fit.

linear regression equation

The linear regression equation is the equation for the line of best fit.

mantissa

In the expression $a \times 10^n$, the variable a is called the mantissa. In scientific notation, the mantissa is greater than or equal to 1 and less than 10.

Example $6.1 \times 10^5 = 610,000$

↑

mantissa

matching list

In the Stroop Test, when the color of the ink matches each color word in a list, the list is called a matching list.

Multiplicative Identity

The number 1 is the multiplicative identity because when 1 is multiplied by any number, the product is that number.

Examples

$a \cdot 1 = a$ $43 \cdot 1 = 43$

Multiplicative Inverse

Two numbers are multiplicative inverses if their product is the multiplicative identity, or 1.

Examples

$9 \cdot \dfrac{1}{9} = 1$ $a \cdot \dfrac{1}{a} = 1$

negative association

On a scatter plot, if the dependent variable decreases as the independent variable increases, then the two variables have a negative association.

Example

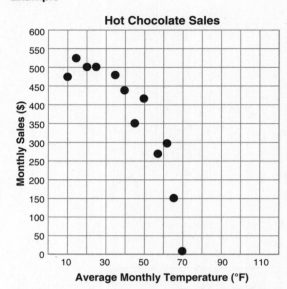

As the average monthly temperature increases, the monthly sales of hot chocolate decreases. So, there is a negative association between average monthly temperature and hot chocolate sales.

negative reciprocal

When the product of two numbers is −1, the numbers are negative reciprocals of one another.

Examples

The negative reciprocal of $\dfrac{3}{7}$ is $\dfrac{-7}{3}$:

$$\frac{3}{7} \times \frac{-7}{3} = \frac{-21}{21} = -1$$

The negative reciprocal of 5 is $\dfrac{-1}{5}$:

$$\frac{5}{1} \times \frac{-1}{5} = \frac{-5}{5} = -1$$

Glossary

non-linear association (non-linear relationship)

Data that have a pattern that is not linear are said to have a non-linear association, or non-linear relationship. Non-linear relationships graphed on a scatter plot have the data points in the shape of a curve.

Example

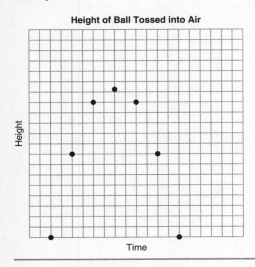

Height of Ball Tossed into Air

nonlinear graph

A nonlinear graph is a graph that is not a line and therefore not a series of collinear points.

non-matching list

In the Stroop Test, when the color of the ink does not match each color word in a list, the list is called a non-matching list.

―――― O ――――

order of magnitude

The order of magnitude is an estimate of size expressed as a power of ten.

Example

The Earth's mass has an <u>order of magnitude</u> of about 10^{24} kilograms.

outlier

An outlier for two-variable data is a point that varies greatly from the overall pattern of the data.

Example

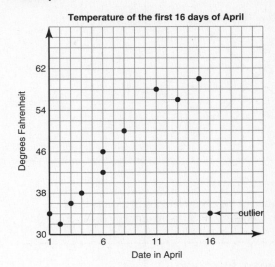

Temperature of the first 16 days of April

output

The second coordinate of an ordered pair in a relation is the output.

―――― P ――――

parallel lines

Parallel lines are lines that lie in the same plane and do not intersect no matter how far they extend. The symbol for parallel is ∥. The symbol for not parallel is ∦.

Example

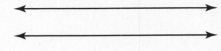

per

Per means "for each" or "for every."

perpendicular lines

Perpendicular lines are lines that intersect at a right angle. The symbol for perpendicular is ⊥. The symbol for not perpendicular is ⊥̸.

Example

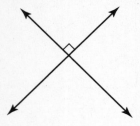

pi

Pi is the ratio of the circumference of a circle to its diameter. Generally, π is approximately 3.14, or $\frac{22}{7}$.

piecewise function

A piecewise function is a function whose equation changes for different parts, or pieces, of the domain.

Example

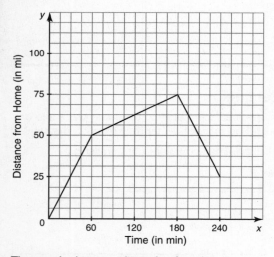

The graph shows a <u>piecewise function.</u>

plane

A plane extends infinitely in all directions in two dimensions and has no thickness.

point of intersection

In a system of linear equations, a point of intersection indicates a solution to both equations.

point of rotation

The point of rotation is the point around which a figure is rotated. The point of rotation can be a point on the figure, inside the figure, or outside the figure.

Example

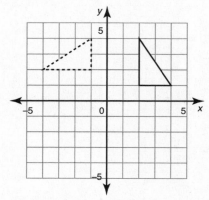

The figure has been rotated 90° counterclockwise. The <u>point of rotation</u> is the origin (0, 0).

point-slope form

The point-slope form of a linear equation that passes through the point (x_1, y_1) and has a slope m is $m(x - x_1) = (y - y_1)$.

Glossary

positive association

On a scatter plot, the two variables have a positive association if, as the independent variable increases, the dependent variable also increases.

Example

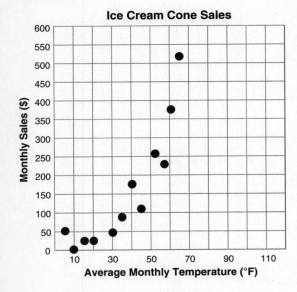

As the average monthly temperature increases, the monthly sales of ice cream cones also increases. So, there is a <u>positive association</u> between average monthly temperature and ice cream cone sales.

postulate

A postulate is a mathematical statement that cannot be proved but is considered true.

power

A power consists of a base and an exponent.

Example base $\longrightarrow 6^2 \longleftarrow$ exponent
<u>power</u>

Power to a Power Rule

The Power to a Power rule states that to simplify a power to a power, keep the base and multiply the exponents.

Examples

$(a^m)^n = a^{mn}$ $(8a^4)^2 = 8a^8$

pre-image

The original figure in a transformation is called the pre-image.

Product Rule of Powers

The Product Rule of Powers states that when multiplying powers with the same base, keep the base and add the exponents.

Examples

$a^m \cdot a^n = a^{m+n}$ $2a^8 \cdot 2a^7 = 2a^{15}$

profit

The profit is the amount of money that you have left after you subtract the costs from the amount of money that you receive.

proof

A proof is a series of steps used to prove the validity of a theorem.

Pythagorean Theorem

The Pythagorean Theorem states: If a and b are the lengths of the legs of a right triangle, and c is the length of the hypotenuse, then $a^2 + b^2 = c^2$.

Example

$0.6^2 + 0.8^2 = 1^2$
$0.36 + 0.64 = 1$

Pythagorean triple

Any set of three positive integers a, b, and c that satisfies the equation $a^2 + b^2 = c^2$ is a Pythagorean triple.

Example

3, 4 and 5 is a <u>Pythagorean triple</u>: $3^2 + 4^2 = 5^2$
$9 + 16 = 25$

Q

quadratic function

A quadratic function is a function that can be written in the form $f(x) = ax^2 + bx + c$.

Quotient Rule of Powers

The Quotient Rule of Powers states that when dividing powers with the same base, keep the base and subtract the exponents.

Examples

$$\frac{a^m}{a_n} = a^{m-n}$$

$$\frac{6b^9}{6b^4} = 6b^5$$

R

radius of a cylinder

The radius of a cylinder is the distance from the center of the base to any point on the base.

radius of a sphere

A segment drawn from the center of the sphere to a point on the sphere is called a radius.

range

The range of a function is the set of all outputs of the function.

rate

A rate is a ratio in which the two quantities being compared are measured in different units.

Example

The speed 60 miles in 2 hours is a rate:

$$\frac{60 \text{ mi}}{2 \text{ h}} = \frac{30 \text{ mi}}{1 \text{ h}}.$$

rate of change

A rate of change is the amount that the dependent value changes for every amount that the independent value changes.

Example

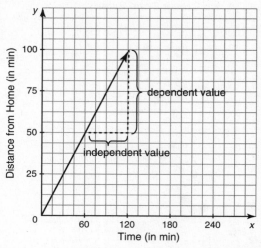

The rate of change shown in this graph is $\frac{50 \text{ mi}}{60 \text{ min}}$, or 50 miles per hour.

rational numbers

Rational numbers are numbers that can be written as $\frac{a}{b}$, where a and b are integers, but b is not equal to 0.

Examples

$4, \frac{1}{2}, \frac{2}{3}, 0.67,$ and $\frac{22}{7}$ are examples of <u>rational numbers</u>.

real numbers

The real numbers consist of all rational numbers and irrational numbers. Real numbers can be represented on the real number line.

Examples

The numbers $-3, 1.25, \frac{11}{4}$, and $\sqrt{13}$ shown below are <u>real numbers</u>.

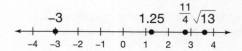

Glossary

reciprocal

When the product of two numbers is 1, the numbers are reciprocals of one another.

Examples

The <u>reciprocal</u> of $\frac{3}{7}$ is $\frac{7}{3}$: $\frac{3}{7} \times \frac{7}{3} = \frac{21}{21} = 1$

The <u>reciprocal</u> of 5 is $\frac{1}{5}$: $\frac{5}{1} \times \frac{1}{5} = \frac{5}{5} = 1$

reduction

When the scale factor is less than one, the image is called a reduction.

reflection

A reflection is a transformation that flips a figure over a reflection line.

Example

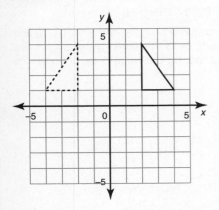

refection line

A reflection line is a line that acts as a mirror so that corresponding points are the same distance from the mirror.

Example

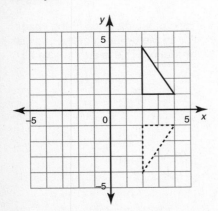

The x-axis is the <u>reflection line</u>.

Reflexive Property of Equality

The Reflexive Property of Equality states that for any real number a, $a = a$.

Example

$7 = 7$

relation

A relation is any set of ordered pairs, or the mapping between a set of inputs and a set of outputs.

relative frequency

A relative frequency is the ratio or percent of occurrences within a category to the total of the category.

right angle

A right angle has a measure of 90° and is indicated by a square in a right triangle.

Example

right angle

right circular cylinder

A right circular cylinder is a cylinder in which the bases are circles and they are aligned one directly above the other.

right triangle

A right triangle is a triangle with exactly one right angle.

Examples

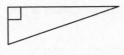

rise

The rise is the vertical distance between two points on a line.

Glossary

rise / run

The ratio $\frac{\text{rise}}{\text{run}}$ is a representation of the rate of change.

Example

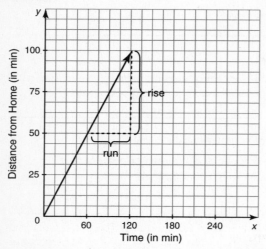

The rate of change shown in this graph is $\frac{50 \text{ mi}}{60 \text{ min}}$, or 50 miles per hour.

rotation

A rotation is a transformation that turns a figure about a fixed point for a given angle.

Example

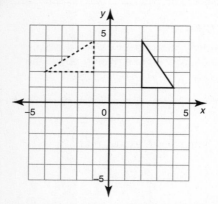

The figure has been rotated 90° counterclockwise about the point (0, 0).

run

The run is the horizontal distance between two points on a line.

same-side exterior angles

Same-side exterior angles are angles formed when a line (transversal) intersects two other lines. These angles are on the same side of the transversal and are outside the other two lines.

Example

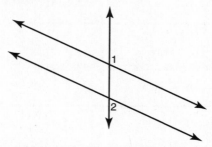

Angles 1 and 2 are <u>same-side exterior angles</u>.

same-side interior angles

Same-side interior angles are angles formed when a line (transversal) intersects two other lines. These angles are on the same side of the transversal and are between the other two lines.

Example

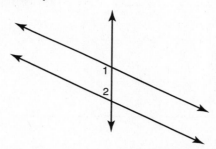

Angles 1 and 2 are <u>same-side interior angles</u>.

scale factor

The scale factor is the ratio of the distance of the image from the center of dilation to the distance of the original figure from the center of dilation. This is also known as the dilation factor.

Example

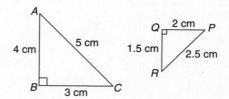

The <u>scale factor</u> from triangle *ABC* to triangle *PQR* is $\frac{1}{2}$.

Glossary

scatter plot

A scatter plot is a graph of a collection of ordered pairs that allows exploration of the relationship between the points.

Example

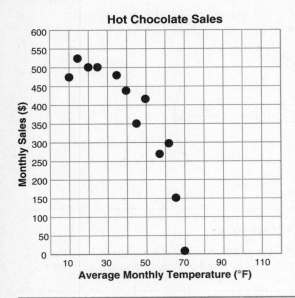

scientific notation

Scientific notation is a way to express a very large or very small number as the product of a number greater than or equal to 1 and less than 10 and a power of 10.

Example

The number 1,345,000,000 is written in scientific notation as 1.345×10^9.

sequence

A sequence is a pattern involving an ordered arrangement of numbers, geometric figures, letters, or other objects.

Side-Angle-Side (SAS) Congruence Theorem

The Side-Angle-Side (SAS) Congruence Theorem states that if two sides and the included angle of one triangle are congruent to the corresponding two sides and the included angle of a second triangle, then the triangles are congruent.

Side-Angle-Side (SAS) Similarity Theorem

The Side-Angle-Side (SAS) Similarity Theorem states that if two pairs of corresponding sides of two triangles are proportional and the included angles are congruent, then the triangles are similar.

Side-Side-Side (SSS) Congruence Theorem

The Side-Side-Side (SSS) Congruence Theorem states that if three sides of one triangle are congruent to the corresponding sides of another triangle, then the triangles are congruent.

Side-Side-Side (SSS) Similarity Theorem

The Side-Side-Side (SSS) Similarity Theorem states that if three pairs of corresponding sides of two triangles are proportional, then the triangles are similar.

similar triangles

Similar triangles are triangles that have the same shape.

skew lines

Skew lines, or non-coplanar lines, are lines that are not located in the same plane.

Example

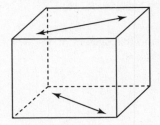

slope

Slope is another mathematical term for rate of change.

Example

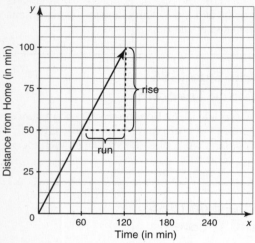

The <u>slope</u> of the line is $\frac{50}{60}$, or $\frac{5}{6}$.

slope-intercept form

The slope-intercept form of a linear equation is $y = mx + b$, where m is the slope of the line and b is the y-intercept.

solution of a linear system

The solution of a linear system is an ordered pair (x, y) that is a solution to both equations in the system. Graphically, the solution is the point of intersection, the point at which two or more lines cross.

Example

$\begin{cases} y = x + 5 \\ y = -2x + 8 \end{cases}$ The solution to this system of equations is (1, 6).

sphere

A sphere is defined as the set of all points in three dimensions that are equidistant from a given point called the center.

Example

Point C is the center of the sphere, and r is the radius of the sphere.

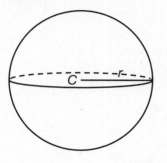

standard form

The standard form of a linear equation is $Ax + By = C$, where A, B, and C are constants and A and B are not both zero.

Stroop Test

The Stroop Test is used to study a person's perception of words and colors by using lists of color words (red, green, black, and blue) that are written in one of the four colors.

substitution method

The substitution method is a process of solving a system of equations by substituting a variable in one equation with an equivalent expression.

supplementary angles

Two angles are supplementary angles if the sum of their angle measures is equal to 180°.

Example

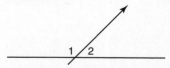

Angles 1 and 2 are <u>supplementary angles</u>.

Symmetric Property of Equality

The Symmetric Property of Equality states that for any real numbers a and b, if $a = b$, then $b = a$

Example

If $\frac{1}{2} = 0.5$, then $0.5 = \frac{1}{2}$

system of linear equations

When two or more linear equations define a relationship between quantities, they form a system of linear equations.

Example

$$\begin{cases} y = x + 5 \\ y = -2x + 8 \end{cases}$$

T

---

theorem

A theorem is a mathematical statement that can be proven using definitions, postulates, and other theorems.

Example

The Pythagorean Theorem states: If a and b are the lengths of the legs of a right triangle and c is the length of the hypotenuse, then $a^2 + b^2 = c^2$.

term

A term of a sequence is an individual number, figure, or letter in the sequence.

Example

2, 7, 12, 17, 22, 27, 32, ...

↑
term

The Transitive Property of Equality

The Transitive Property of Equality states that for any real numbers a, b, and c, if $a = b$ and $b = c$, then $a = c$

Example

If $\frac{1}{2} = 0.5$, and $0.5 = 50\%$, then $\frac{1}{2} = 50\%$

transformation

A transformation is the mapping, or movement, of all the points of a figure in a plane according to a common operation.

Examples

Translations, reflections, and rotations are examples of transformations.

translation

A translation is a transformation that "slides" each point of a figure the same distance and direction.

Example

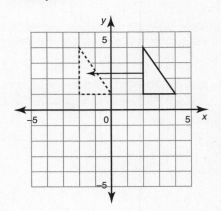

transversal

A transversal is a line that intersects two or more lines at distinct points. A transversal is said to "cut" the lines.

Example

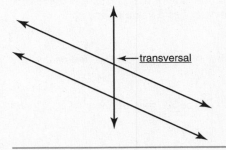

trend line

When a line of best fit is used, the line and its equation are often referred to as a model of the data, or a trend line.

Triangle Sum Theorem

The Triangle Sum Theorem states that the sum of the measures of the three interior angles of a triangle is equal to 180°.

two-step equation

A two-step equation requires that two inverse operations be performed in order to isolate the variable.

two-variable data set

When collecting information on two separate characteristics for the same person or thing to determine if there is a relationship between them, those characteristics can be described as a two-variable data set.

Example

If you collect data about your classmates' heights and shoe sizes, then the data you collect would be called a two-variable data set.

two-way table

A two-way table displays categorical data that shows the number of data points that fall into each group for two variables. One variable is divided into rows, and the other is divided into columns.

Example

	April	May	June
7ᵗʰ graders	ɦɦɫ	//	
8ᵗʰ graders	ɦɦɫ ɦɦɫ	///	ɦɦɫ

Glossary

U

unit rate

A unit rate is a comparison of two measurements in which the denominator has a value of one unit.

Example

The speed 60 miles in 2 hours can be written as a unit rate: $\frac{60 \text{ mi}}{2 \text{ h}} = \frac{30 \text{ mi}}{1 \text{ h}}$.

The unit rate is $\frac{30 \text{ mi}}{1 \text{ h}}$, or 30 miles per hour.

V

Venn diagram

A Venn diagram uses circles to show how elements among sets of numbers or objects are related.

Example

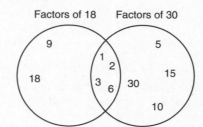

vertical angles

Vertical angles are two non-adjacent angles that are formed by two intersecting lines.

Example

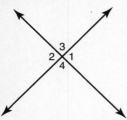

Angles 1 and 2 are <u>vertical angles.</u>
Angles 3 and 4 are <u>vertical angles.</u>

vertical line test

The vertical line test is a visual method of determining whether a relation represented as a graph is a function. To apply the vertical line test, consider all of the vertical lines that could be drawn on the graph of a relation. If any of the vertical lines intersect the graph of the relation at more than one point, then the relation is not a function.

Example

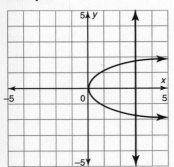

The line drawn at $x = 3$ crosses two points on the graph, so the relation is not a function.

Y

y-intercept

The y-intercept is the y-coordinate of the point where a graph crosses the y-axis. The y-intercept can also be written in the form $(0, y)$.

Z

Zero Power Rule

The Zero Power Rule states that the zero power of any number except for 0 is 1.

Examples

$a^0 = 1$ $\qquad\qquad$ $6^0 = 1$

INDEX

Index

Index

Index

Index

of hypotenuse, 330
of unknown side lengths of right
triangles, 335–348
mathematical properties used to
discover, 330–334
right triangles determined with,
330–333, 346
Pythagorean triple, 337

Q

Quadratic functions, 111, 114
Quantities, variable and constant, 94
Quotient Rule of Powers
identifying, 729–738
in scientific notation, 722–724
in simplifying powers, 698–700,
704–706, 709
summary of, 700

R

Radius
of a cone, 763
of a cylinder, 748–749, 757–758, 763
of a sphere, 776–778, 780, 782,
784, 787
Range
definition of, 69
of functions, 69, 73, 88, 109, 111,
113, 258–259
of problem situations, 96, 132, 149,
247–248, 250, 252
Rate
definition of, 131
as a unit rate, 139, 146–147, 150
Rate of change
context used to determine,
163–170, 187
definition of, 131
equation used to determine,
171–183, 187
first differences and, 159–161
formal method for determining,
151–152, 179
formula for calculating, 152–156,
165, 170
graph used to determine,
129–143, 187
informal method for determining,
151, 156, 179
negative, 135
ordered pairs used to determine, 152,
157–161
"per" used in, 131
rise over run ratio in, 134–136
slope-intercept form and, 179,
196–197, 199–201
substitution used to determine, 152
table used to determine, 145–161, 187
unit, 132, 137, 142, 149, 154
y-intercept and, 198
Rational numbers, 288–290
definition of, 288
number line used to compare and
order, 284
Ratios
definition of, 131

with denominator of 0 (undefined),
142
dilations of triangles and, 482–483,
489
Real numbers, 298–304
classifying numbers in, 298–300
definition of, 298
properties of, 301–304
Reciprocals, 574
Rectangle, determining length of,
358–359
Reductions, 482–483, 488–489, 510,
512, 514–515
Reflection, 415–421
definition of, 416
of geometric figures on the
coordinate plane, 415–421
over axes, 416–419
over horizontal and vertical lines,
419–420
of parallelogram, 417–419
of triangles on a coordinate plane,
436–438, 440
Reflection line
definition of, 416
in line transformations, 581–582
Reflexive Property of Equality, 303
Relations
definition of, 69
as equations, 77
as functions, 70, 75, 78, 83
graphical representations of, 74–76,
88–90, 95, 109, 111, 113
as ordered pairs, 68–71
as sequences, 73
Relative frequency
of categorical data, 906, 909
definition of, 906
Relative frequency bar graphs, 915–917
Relative frequency tables, 908, 915, 922
Repeating decimals, 292–294
Repunit numbers, 283
Response variables. See Dependent
variables
Right circular cylinder, 748
Right triangles, side lengths of
converse of the Pythagorean
Theorem and, 335–348
diagonal of a square and, 315
exploring, 315–329
hypotenuse, 314–315, 319, 323,
327–330, 344, 353
identifying, 314
isosceles right triangle, 315, 343
legs, 314
Pythagorean Theorem and, 330–348
solving problems involving, 315–329
unknown lengths of, determining,
335–348
Rise, 134–136
Rise over run ratio
for graphs, 134–136
for tables, 153
Rotation, 407–414
angle of, 409
definition of, 408–409

of geometric figures on the
coordinate plane, 407–414
of parallelogram, 411–412
of perpendicular lines in line
transformations, 579–580
point of, 409, 414
of trapezoid, 412
of triangles on a coordinate plane,
433–435, 439
Rounding values, 856, 865, 868
Run, 134–136

S

Same-side exterior angles
definition of, 548
formed by two lines and a transversal,
measuring, 556
on maps, 551, 553–554
relationships of the measures of,
557, 561
in transversals, 548
Same-side interior angles, 547–548
definition of, 547
formed by two lines and a transversal,
measuring, 556
on maps, 551, 553–554
relationships of the measures of,
557, 561
in transversals, 547–548
Scale factor (dilation factor), 480, 482,
510, 512, 514–515
Scatter plots
associations in, 809–812
clustered data values in, 809
for collected data, connecting,
817–824
creating and interpreting, 800–803
with graphing calculator, 804–805
dependent variables on, 808,
810–812, 891–893, 896, 913
to display and analyze two-variable
relationships, 797–806
to display and interpret data,
818–820
human wrist chain experiment and,
818–820
independent variables on, 808,
810–812, 891–893, 896, 913
linear relationships on, 895, 897–898
in lines of best fit, 833, 838, 846–852,
857, 859, 866, 877–879
non-linear relationships on, 890–898
no relationships on, 897–898
ordered pairs on, 891–893
outliers in, 813–814
patterns in, interpreting, 802, 807–815
in Stroop Test, 857–860
Scientific notation
adding and subtracting numbers in,
724–727
definition of, 712
expressing numbers in, 711–718
order of magnitude, 712
standard form, 717–718
very large, 714–715
very small, 716–718

Index

Index